FOREWORD

It is almost nine years since Sir Michael Latham in h[...]ucung the Team" called for a new culture in the construction industry - partnering - and for a new family of contracts to facilitate this change. In 1998 Sir John Egan in "Rethinking Construction" made it clear that, while the industry must seriously address its processes, world-class performance would only be secured by establishing integrated teams - by partnering the supply team and chain.

While the industry's movers and shakers eagerly responded and adopted partnering arrangements based upon charters and bespoke contracts, it was only with the publication by the ACA of PPC2000 that the full response to Latham was put in place. When followed by SPC2000 the industry at last had a "new family of contracts" to equip it for the twenty first century.

Exemplified by the Rethinking Construction Demonstration Projects and including broad sectors of the industry, considerable progress has been and continues to be made in improving performance based upon multi-party partnering arrangements. This is fast becoming the contractual method of choice for a growing number of intelligent clients.

None of the proponents of partnering have pretended it is an easy option, and as with all innovation, progress has been limited by lack of confidence and a ready source of "how to" information. This Guide now provides a manual that fills the gap.

This Guide to PPC2000 and SPC2000 is rooted firmly in practical feedback from many industry professionals working on real projects, based on more than three years of hard-won experience and rigorous analysis. It provides in a logical form the process of formulating an agreement and addresses the many issues that arise when using a partnering contract. Truly comprehensive and expressed in a readily understandable language, it is the final step to removing the barriers to effective partnering for all.

I am pleased to have been asked to write this foreword and even more pleased to support this Guide. It does not compromise but rather enhances the principles of "Rethinking Construction", and will help all of us to take forward partnering as the norm with the desired achievement of more successful projects.

Alan Crane CBE
Chair, Rethinking Construction

CONTENTS

CONTENTS

CONTENTS

GUIDE to the ACA Project Partnering Contracts PPC2000 and SPC2000

CHAPTER 1 - INTRODUCTION

PPC2000 has become a mainstream contractual option for teams who wish to adopt an integrated approach to project procurement. At the time of writing this guide (May 2003), it is two and a half years since Sir John Egan launched PPC2000 and it has already been adopted, to the author's knowledge, on projects totalling over £5billion.

PPC2000 responds to a recognised need in the construction and engineering industries for a process document that integrates the roles of all team members and that covers both the pre-construction and construction phases of any project. It has been accepted as a robust and balanced document by partnering teams in the public, voluntary and private sectors. It is being used to procure successful projects across a wide range of needs including office, residential, educational, healthcare, leisure, public buildings, rail and highways.

PPC2000 is complemented by the SPC2000 ACA Standard Form of Specialist Contract for Project Partnering and the Scottish Supplement PPC(S)2000.

Many people were responsible for securing the success of PPC2000. They include John Wright and the members of the Construction Industry Council Partnering Task Force whose radical ideas and model heads of terms gave rise to PPC2000; the teams led by David Hill and Noel Foley for backing the first PPC2000 prototypes on major office and residential projects; the author's colleagues in the Projects and Construction Group of Solicitors Trowers & Hamlins, including my secretary Ann Orsler, for their work on the draft PPC2000 documents; Fiona Griffiths and the ACA Council for promoting PPC2000 documents and establishing the Association of Partnering Advisers; all of the clients, constructors, consultants, specialists, insurers and funders who have used PPC2000 on such a wide range of projects; Sir Michael Latham for reviewing the draft of PPC2000 in considerable detail; and Alan Crane CBE, and the various arms of "Rethinking Construction", for driving forward construction reform and recognising the role of PPC2000 in this process.

This guide provides background to the PPC2000 and SPC2000 Forms of Contract and the PPC(S)2000 Supplement. It describes the key features of these documents, goes through the PPC2000 project processes and provides a clause by clause commentary.

This guide also aims to clarify why PPC2000 provides for the role of *"Partnering Adviser"* and explains the added value that a Partnering Adviser can bring to a partnered project. It identifies ten common pitfalls of the project partnering process which PPC2000 seeks to avoid, and of which partnering teams should remain wary.

PPC2000 has been extensively used without the support of a published guide, and partnering teams will continue to make their own decisions as to the ways in which a contract can help them to obtain best value and achieve a successfully completed project. Neither PPC2000 nor this guide are a substitute for personal relationships, industry experience and the will to escape the constraints of adversarial, unimaginative ways of working. What this guide does aim to do is explain why PPC2000 has a place in the range of available procurement options and make it easier for all team members to put PPC2000 into practice.

CHAPTER 2 - BACKGROUND TO PPC2000 AND SPC2000

2.1 WHAT IS PPC2000?

PPC2000 is the first standard form of Project Partnering Contract. It was launched in September 2000 by Sir John Egan, Chairman of the Construction Task Force, who described it as a *"blow for freedom"*. It provides a foundation and route map for the partnering process and can be applied to any type of partnered project in any jurisdiction.

PPC2000 was drafted by the author of this guide and other members of the Projects and Construction Group of solicitors Trowers & Hamlins, with input drawn from the experience of a wide variety of project partnering teams and their advisers. It is a direct response to the recommendations identified by the Construction Task Force in their July 1998 report *"Rethinking Construction"* (often referred to as *"the Egan Report"*) and incorporates ideas set out in the Construction Industry Council Guide to Project Team Partnering (the *"CIC Guide"*). PPC2000 was developed through prototypes tested on a variety of pilot projects.

PPC2000 has been formally endorsed by the Construction Industry Council, the Movement for Innovation, the Local Government Task Force, the Housing Forum and the Construction Best Practice Programme. (The latter four bodies are now integrated under the title *"Rethinking Construction"* represented by the Rethinking Construction logo alongside the Construction Best Practice logo under the banner *"Constructing Excellence"*).

To focus firstly on the CIC Guide, this was originally launched by Nicholas Raynsford MP, then Minister for Construction, in July 2000 and a second edition was launched by Sir Michael Latham in March 2002. It was the work of a pan-industry group of construction professionals, and includes clear and concise guidelines for project partnering. It also incorporates model heads of terms that form the basis of PPC2000. The CIC Guide recognised expressly the need for a new form of contract, in particular one that integrated both the team and the procurement process, and states:-

> *"An effective contract can play a central role in partnering. It sets out the common and agreed rules; it helps define the goals and how to achieve them; it states the agreed mechanism for managing the risks and the rewards; it lays down the guidelines for resolving disputes..... Creating a contract that can accommodate those aspirations is clearly of paramount importance in the development of partnering."*

In order to understand the principles underlying PPC2000, it is also necessary to consider the 1994 report of Sir Michael Latham, *"Constructing The Team"*. Sir Michael recommended the following principles for a modern construction contract:

- duties of fairness, teamwork, mutual co-operation and shared financial motivation;

- clearly defined roles and duties in a fully integrated document;

- a contract that is suitable for all projects and any procurement route;

- drafting in straightforward language;

- agreed allocation of risks for each project with changes priced in advance;

- flexibility as to payments with clear payment entitlements;

- incentives for exceptional performance;

- mechanisms for avoidance of conflict and speedy dispute resolution.

Sir Michael Latham has reviewed PPC2000 in detail and has confirmed that it embodies all his recommended principles for a modern construction contract. He described PPC2000 in Building Magazine (10 May 2002) as *"the full monty of partnering and modern best practice".*

2.2 WHAT ABOUT EGAN?

The central theme of the Egan Report, and more recently the report of the Strategic Forum *"Accelerating Change"* (October 2002), is that substantial improvements can be achieved in the procurement of projects through the early integration of the team and the procurement process. These are the means identified not only to eliminate the deeply embedded blame culture that so easily triggers construction disputes, but also to improve efficiency, eliminate waste and maximise best performance from all project team members. The reforms recommended by the Egan Report offered incremental commercial benefits, not only to the client but also to all other team members, by way of:-

- reduced costs

- reduced time

- reduced defects

- reduced accidents

- increased predictability

- increased productivity

- increased turnover and profit.

The Egan Report identified partnering as the medium to achieve these benefits, both through integration of the team and through integration of the procurement process. At the time the Egan Report relied on the experience of leading innovators in the UK. Since then, a much wider range of clients, constructors, consultants and specialists have adopted partnering, with impressive results on all of the above counts. An illustration of this appears in *"Accelerating Change"*, where statistics confirm that the Demonstration Projects for 2001 achieved significantly better results than the industry average against all of the headings of cost, time, defects, accidents, predictability, productivity and profitability.

2.3 WHAT IS PROJECT PARTNERING?

Partnering has developed as a set of collaborative management techniques necessary to bring about cultural change in the construction industry. In order to measure up to the full range of practical challenges that arise during the course of the design, supply and construction process, partnering teams should ensure that the new collaborative culture is fully embedded in all project procedures in place of the adversarial alternatives. To do this, cultural change needs to be combined with clear, robust and fully integrated techniques for bringing together and holding together the project team. For all team members to understand what each other have agreed to do and when they will do it is fundamental in order to translate the new culture into a sustainable means of achieving improved results. This is the purpose of PPC2000.

Project partnering should be distinguished from strategic alliancing. The latter was defined by the CIC Guide as the grouping of a number of projects in order to obtain the benefit of long-term relationships. PPC2000 is a contract for the partnering of a single project, as a medium to bring demonstrable benefit to that project and to partnering team members even if the same team do not have the opportunity to work together on successive further projects. In practice, PPC2000 is often also used for procurement of each project within a strategic alliancing arrangement.

2.4 WHY USE A NEW FORM OF CONTRACT?

There are many standard form building contracts and professional appointments in existence. Why should a new form of contract make any difference to the success of a project?

To quote from the CIC Guide, *"There has been much talk in the press and comments from industry experts that may suggest that partnering is not about contracts. This is partly true. What partnering is not about is for each party to use contracts to strengthen their position at the expense of others and the overall project. It is not about the conflict and the lengthy and costly disputes that are too frequently the end result when parties are bound by intrinsically adversarial contracts."*.

The motivation behind PPC2000 is to provide a more positive role for the contract, namely to describe the way in which a project partnering team really works together. A clearly drafted project partnering contract should provide a structure that underpins trust and co-operation between the members of the partnering team and that in addition makes project partnering more accessible - it should demystify the project partnering process.

To quote again from the CIC Guide: *"An effective partnering contract should support the full partnering team and aim to deliver an integrated project process. Logically, it should replace any of the existing standard contract forms"*.

2.5 WHY DO YOU NEED A PARTNERING CONTRACT?

A number of myths have built up around partnering, including firstly the suggestion that you can partner with no form of contract at all; secondly the suggestion that you can partner with any form of contract whatsoever because you do not need to refer to it; and thirdly the suggestion that the only really important document is a *"Partnering Charter"*.

As to the first suggestion, it is difficult to find any public or private sector organisation that does not need to know the terms on which it commits or expects to receive a substantial sum of money.

As to the second suggestion, for team members to sign any form of contract whatsoever and then not refer to it is both a dangerous mistake and a sad reflection on the irrelevance of many construction industry standard forms. If a contract is not consulted during the course of the project, it cannot operate as a process document and cannot assist the progress of the project itself. Worse than that, if a contract is left unread, it is unlikely that team members will be fully familiar with its terms, and they may be unpleasantly surprised when (in the event of a discrepancy) those terms override the other contract documents.

GUIDE to PPC2000 & SPC2000   © ACA and Trowers & Hamlins 2003

PPC2000 plays a more active role in the contract structure. It is a process document, commencing at the earliest point in the formation of a team and acting as a hub to describe the practical working relationships between project team members and the practical processes necessary to develop designs, manage risk, formulate a full supply chain and procure a completed project.

As to the third suggestion that you only really need a Partnering Charter, this is generally a very brief document intended to capture headline statements of the agreed values, goals and priorities of a partnering team. A Partnering Charter is not a working document and does not describe specific roles, responsibilities and relationships. To quote once more from the CIC Guide, *"While it is recognised that partnering charters have served a valuable role, the time is right to see a fully integrated approach, so that the relationships and processes required for effective partnering are not at odds with the contractual rules and relationships of partnering team members"*.

That is not to say that Partnering Charters do not continue to play a role, and this is recognised in clauses 2.6 (v) and 5.6 (ii) of the PPC2000 Partnering Terms *(see also Chapter 6)*.

2.6 WHAT IS SPC2000?

SPC2000 is the first standard form of Specialist Contract for Project Partnering and was launched by Sir Michael Latham in March 2002. It allows the main contractor to enter into contracts with its sub-contractors, including those sub-contractors who also sign PPC2000, in a manner that is consistent with PPC2000 and further integrates the agreed relationships and project processes *(see also Chapter 7)*.

SPC2000 recognises the importance, highlighted in the Egan Report, of the additional contributions that sub-contractors can bring to a project if they are appointed sufficiently early in the project process and if they are integrated into the project partnering team.

SPC2000 focuses on involvement of sub-contractors in project design and risk management from the earliest possible stage. It also encourages open-book pricing and collaborative working throughout all stages of the project process.

SPC2000 follows the format of PPC2000 throughout, and allows the main contractor to contract with all sub-contractors on terms that are wholly consistent with PPC2000 and the objectives of project partnering.

CHAPTER 3 - KEY FEATURES OF PPC2000

In what way does PPC2000 deal with areas not covered in other standard form contracts?

The fundamental differences are that:

- PPC2000 integrates the entire project team under a single multi-party contract;
- PPC2000 covers the entire duration of the procurement process;
- PPC2000 introduces effective controls to support partnered project management.

3.1 THE MULTI-PARTY APPROACH

PPC2000 is a single multi-party contract relating to an agreed *"Project"* and *"Site"*, whereby the *"Client"*, the *"Constructor"* (i.e. the main contractor) and all *"Consultants"* (i.e. the Client's appointed advisers) work together as a team under the same terms and conditions. All or certain *"Specialists"* (i.e. the Constructor's sub-contractors, sub-consultants or suppliers) can also sign PPC2000 as members of the *"Partnering Team"*. Definitions of these terms and of all other words and expressions used in PPC2000 are set out in PPC2000 Appendix 1.

The Client works with other Partnering Team members through one integrated contract rather than through numerous separate two-party contracts. This substantially reduces the risk of gaps or overlaps between the different roles and responsibilities of Partnering Team members and creates mutual duties of care between all Partnering Team members.

In a series of two-party contracts, the only common contracting party would be the Client, who then becomes inextricably involved in the operation of all interfaces between other team members. PPC2000 as a multi-party contract establishes new direct contractual links between all team members, so that they have an opportunity and an obligation to rely on each other directly.

It is worth contrasting a multi-party contract with the alternative of creating additional contractual links through the use of collateral warranties. Collateral warranties establish almost entirely duties (and almost never rights) on the part of whoever provides the warranties, and do not in any way integrate the terms of the various underlying contracts. PPC2000 establishes a level playing field of both rights and duties between all Partnering Team members as well as an open arrangement where all of them are fully aware of each other's roles, responsibilities and relationships.

3.2 INTEGRATED PROCESS

It is important that the design and risk management expertise of the Constructor and Specialists should be captured prior to start on Site. Nearly all other standard form building contracts provide for immediate mobilisation and start on Site and do not cover the pre-construction phase of the Project at all. PPC2000 provides for the creation of the Partnering Team at the earliest possible opportunity during the pre-construction phase, thereby establishing a contractual framework governing the development of designs, the management of risk, the agreement of works and services packages, and the build up of agreed prices.

PPC2000 focuses on design development during both the pre-construction phase and the construction phase, with maximum Constructor and Specialist contributions prior to start on Site. Also, it provides a system to identify and approve any Constructor's *"Direct Labour Packages"* and any *"Preferred Specialist"* packages, and to build up the remaining members of the supply chain during the pre-construction phase (or later if so agreed), having

GUIDE to PPC2000 & SPC2000   © ACA and Trowers & Hamlins 2003

pre-agreed the Constructor's *"Profit"*, *"Central Office Overheads"*, *"Site Overheads"* and other known costs. PPC2000 thereby uses open-book pricing to ensure a transparent picture of cost, agreed by all parties and built up in logical stages to achieve the required level of detail and certainty. This in turn forms the foundation for supply chain partnering.

Creation under PPC2000 of a Partnering Team at the earliest opportunity linking design development, price build-up and supply chain appointments to the agreed Project *"Budget"*, and requiring rigorous analysis and management of any priced risks, also ensures that prices are finalised with minimum contingencies. By this means a fixed price (the *"Agreed Maximum Price"*) can be established ahead of start on Site, with full supporting details and only such estimated items or priced risks as the Client and other Partnering Team members may agree. This provides the same degree of price certainty as traditional procurement arrangements but with the support of *"Open-book"* pricing and new opportunities during the pre-construction phase for *"Value Engineering"*, *"Value Management"* and *"Risk Management"* to identify improvements and strip out savings. Open-book cost information also provides a solid foundation for agreement of any later *"Changes"* and for settlement of any claims arising from delay or disruption.

3.3 CONTROLS

PPC2000 contains a number of new team-based controls. A *"Partnering Timetable"* governs all activities of the Partnering Team during the pre-construction phase of the Project prior to start on Site, and a *"Project Timetable"* governs those activities during the construction phase of the Project after start on Site. These documents represent an essential tool for good project management. If Partnering Team members are asked to agree specific periods of time for their respective activities at each stage of the Project, this should avoid over-optimistic estimates and provide a clearly understood, logical basis for efficient team-working.

Additional controls under PPC2000 include sign-off at all key stages. Signature of the *"Project Partnering Agreement"* creates the Partnering Team and establishes the system by which the parties will work towards start on Site. Signature of a *"Joining Agreement"* sets out the role of any new Partnering Team member and signature of a *"Pre-Possession Agreement"* establishes any authority for early work on or off Site. However, signature of a *"Commencement Agreement"* is required before the Partnering Team members are fully authorised to proceed with the Project on Site - and this takes place only when all agreed pre-conditions have been satisfied (*see also Chapter 4*).

Other controls include an agreed commitment to reducing, managing and sharing risks (particularly during the period prior to start on Site), encouragement of measured performance against agreed Key Performance Indicators (*"KPIs"*) and provision for incentives to reward exceptional performance.

Where difficulties arise, PPC2000 seeks to control these through an *"Early Warning"* system and the operation of the *"Core Group"*, comprising individuals representing Partnering Team members whose joint role is to review and stimulate the progress of the Project. PPC2000 also contains a joint commitment to alternative problem resolution - offering reference of a dispute to a *"Problem-Solving Hierarchy"*, then to the Core Group and then to conciliation, mediation or other agreed approaches. All of these steps represent a series of controlled alternatives to the statutory right of adjudication.

Finally, in accordance with the recommendations of the CIC Partnering Task Force, PPC2000 includes the support mechanism of an independent party acting as *"Partnering Adviser"*, owing a duty of care to all Partnering Team members to provide fair and constructive advice as to the partnering process, the development of the partnering relationships and the operation of the *"Partnering Contract"*.

CHAPTER 4 - PPC2000 PROCESSES

PPC2000 is a process document that governs the activities and relationships of all Partnering Team members in clearly defined stages during the pre-construction phase and the construction phase of a Project. Before going through the PPC2000 clauses in detail (*see Chapter 6*), it is worth setting out in straightforward terms the stages of a partnered Project under PPC2000.

4.1 PRE-PPC2000: ASSEMBLING THE PARTNERING TEAM

Project partnering offers an opportunity for significant changes in the traditional roles of all team members. The timing, nature and extent of each party's contribution should depend on the added value that they offer rather than on their assumed position in an industry hierarchy.

Clearly there is a period prior to signature of the PPC2000 Project Partnering Agreement during which the Client establishes an initial *"Project Brief"* and a Budget for the Project and selects Partnering Team members. It is likely that a design Consultant and a cost Consultant will be appointed at this stage to draw up the Project Brief and advise on the Project Budget, but it is also possible that these documents may be produced or contributed to by the Client in-house or by the Constructor or a key Specialist.

Where a Client wishes to use the preliminary services of a design Consultant or cost Consultant (or a Constructor or Specialist) prior to the signature of a PPC2000 Project Partnering Agreement, interim letters of appointment may be appropriate. These should include a statement that each party will sign up to PPC2000 (and that PPC2000 will cover all of its work) once the Project Brief and Project Budget are sufficiently clear and the Partnering Team is created. Advice should be obtained from the Partnering Adviser (*see also Chapter 9*) if interim letters of appointment are proposed, and these can be drafted in a simple form that cross-refers to relevant PPC2000 Partnering Terms. In practice, Clients and other prospective Partnering Team members usually work on an informal basis during the relatively short period until the PPC2000 Project Partnering Agreement is entered into.

Partnering Team members may be selected on a negotiated basis, particularly if they have worked together successfully before and if the Client is not subject to legal or regulatory obligations to go through a tendering procedure. However, where negotiation is not the appropriate or permitted approach, the Client will need to draw up selection documents, such as an invitation to tender or invitation to negotiate, and to go through the steps necessary to select Partnering Team members on the basis of best value against clearly established criteria.

In order to get the selection process started, the CIC Guide (in its section *"How do I select the right partners?"*), recommends that *"One of the first appointments may be the partnering adviser, whether a client undertakes work regularly or not"* and that his or her role at this stage *"is to facilitate the smooth creation and development of the project partnering team"* including to act as a *"guide in the selection and partnering process"*. The role of the Partnering Adviser is distinct from the role of an early design Consultant in drawing up the Project Brief or the role of an early cost Consultant in drawing up the Project Budget. It is also distinct from the later role of a *"Facilitator" (see also Chapter 9.1)*.

For example, the Partnering Adviser has an important role to play in distinguishing the selection documents on a partnered Project from the selection documents used in a traditional tender process. As well as a clear statement of the Client's commitment to the principles of partnering, the selection documents should reflect clearly the structure

GUIDE to PPC2000 & SPC2000   © ACA and Trowers & Hamlins 2003

of the PPC2000 relationships and processes. They should, for example, make clear how selection will be based on best value, including not only price but also experience of partnering and structured proposals for pursuing the Client's stated objectives in line with the recommendations and targets set out in the Egan Report. In practice, the Partnering Adviser generally prepares the selection documents working in close co-operation with the parties responsible for drawing up the Project Brief and Project Budget.

4.2 PPC2000 STRUCTURE AND LAYOUT

PPC2000 is set out as a single published document comprising the following:-

- Project Partnering Agreement *(see section 4.3 below)*;

- *"Partnering Terms" (see Chapter 6);*

- Appendix 1, *"Definitions"*;

- Appendix 2, Form of Joining Agreement *(see section 4.4 below)*;

- Appendix 3 Part 1, Form of Pre-Possession Agreement *(see section 4.5 below);*

- Appendix 3 Part 2, Form of Commencement Agreement *(see section 4.6 below);*

- Appendix 4 - Insurance of Project and Site, Third Party Liability Insurance, Professional Indemnity or Product Liability Insurance, and Insurance - General (all by reference to clause 19 of the Partnering Terms);

- Appendix 5 - Conciliation, Adjudication and Arbitration (if applicable) (all by reference to clause 27 of the Partnering Terms).

During the course of a PPC2000 Project, the Partnering Team members will sign not only the Project Partnering Agreement but also a Commencement Agreement and potentially one or more Joining Agreements and (as between the Client and the Constructor) one or more Pre-Possession Agreements. For practical purposes, any of these published forms may need to be reprinted in order to accommodate appropriate Project-specific details. Enquiries as to the availability of such documents in paper form and on line should be addressed to the ACA at the contact details on the inside front cover of this guide.

PPC2000 is unusual in that, unlike many standard form contracts, it does not state details of the parties at the beginning of the Project Partnering Agreement, Joining Agreement, Pre-Possession Agreement or Commencement Agreement. Instead each form states the parties' names and contact details only at the end of the document where each of them executes it. Creation of each PPC2000 document can be by signing or execution as a deed, and in this guide the term *"signing"* covers both options.

PPC2000 is specifically designed to allow flexibility in the roles and responsibilities of Partnering Team members and in the agreement of key issues such as the authority of the *"Client Representative"* (clause 5.2 of the Partnering Terms), the *"Design Team"* members and the design development process (clause 8 of the Partnering Terms), the use of incentives and KPI targets (clause 13 of the Partnering Terms), the treatment of risk (clause 18 of the Partnering Terms), the methods of payment (clause 20 of the Partnering Terms) and the agreed duties of care (clause 22 of the Partnering Terms).

Each of the Project Partnering Agreement, Joining Agreement, Pre-Possession Agreement and Commencement Agreement require Project-specific details to be inserted wherever there are blank spaces. The wording of these insertions should utilise PPC2000 defined words and expressions where appropriate (as set out in PPC2000 Appendix 1). All insertions in any PPC2000 document should be carefully formulated as they will impact directly on the agreed roles, responsibilities, risks and other obligations assumed by each Partnering Team member, and advice should be obtained from the Partnering Adviser.

The CIC Guide suggests that it is the role of the Partnering Adviser to *"record and document the project partnering team relationships, the commitments made by each party and their expectations in a multi-party partnering contract"*. The rationale for this is to ensure that the documents are prepared by someone who is outside the Partnering Team, has relevant expertise and owes a duty of care to all Partnering Team members. Use of the Partnering Adviser for this purpose should therefore avoid (or at least defer) the need for individual Partnering Team members to appoint separate advisers with no team-based duty of care, who may then (with their individual Clients' best interests in mind) provide conflicting advice. Differing views from separate advisers can create delay in completion of the PPC2000 documents and, particularly where some parties can afford more advice than others, can undermine the spirit of mutual trust and co-operation between Partnering Team members (*see also Chapter 9*).

As to the contractual effect of each insertion, in the left-hand margin of the Project Partnering Agreement and Commencement Agreement there are cross-references to specific Partnering Terms, and the relevant parts of each document should be read together with those Partnering Terms in order to establish their contractual effect.

4.3 PROJECT PARTNERING AGREEMENT *(See also Appendix 10 Flowchart A and Appendix 1 Project Partnering Agreement Checklist)*

When appropriate Partnering Team members have been selected, the PPC2000 Project Partnering Agreement should be signed immediately. This should be as far in advance as possible of start on Site in order to allow adequate periods of time during the pre-construction phase for the Client, Constructor, Consultants and Specialists to participate in organised processes of design development and risk management activities, and in the finalisation of supply chain members and agreement of accurate prices.

The facility for entering into clear contractual arrangements to govern the pre-construction phase is a significant innovation under PPC2000 and an important feature in a properly integrated project partnering process.

At the point of executing the Project Partnering Agreement the Partnering Team members should include a Client, a Constructor and a Client Representative. They should generally also include one or more designers (who may be Consultants and/or Specialists), a cost Consultant and possibly one or more supply and/or construction Specialists.

There may be further Consultants and Specialists who remain to be selected following signature of the Project Partnering Agreement. These should still be identified in the Project Partnering Agreement as Consultants or Specialists as the case may be, with reference to their professional disciplines or trades if specific organisations have not yet been identified.

The *"Partnering Documents"* that will accompany the PPC2000 Project Partnering Agreement should comprise the Project Brief provided by the Client and the initial *"Project Proposals"* provided by the Constructor, each with input from Consultants and Specialists as agreed and each to a sufficient level of detail for the Partnering Team members to agree their pre-construction roles and responsibilities. There should be an

GUIDE to PPC2000 & SPC2000 © ACA and Trowers & Hamlins 2003

initial *"Price Framework"* stating the Client's Budget (if known), the Constructor's agreed Profit, Central Office Overheads and Site Overheads, other known costs and a statement as to the Constructor's proposed costing of risk and any consequent contingencies. There should be at least provisional agreement as to incentives, KPIs and related targets. There should be details of any Consultants and Specialists forming part of the Partnering Team with clear statements of their roles, responsibilities and payment entitlements. Most importantly, in order to justify the early signature of the Project Partnering Agreement, there should be a clear Partnering Timetable governing the activities and interfaces of all Partnering Team members during the pre-construction phase through to the date proposed for start on Site *(see also Chapter 5).*

Once signed up, the PPC2000 Project Partnering Agreement will govern the activities of all Partnering Team members during the pre-construction phase, including the development of designs, the completion of the supply chain through the appointment of additional Specialist sub-consultants, sub-contractors and suppliers, and the development of an Agreed Maximum Price supported by a detailed Price Framework. It will also govern agreed activities during this period in relation to Risk Management, Value Engineering and Value Management.

All activities during the pre-construction phase should be agreed to be undertaken within the timescales set out in the Partnering Terms and the Partnering Timetable, and by stated members of the Partnering Team and Design Team as appropriate.

4.4 JOINING AGREEMENTS *(See also Appendix 2 Joining Agreement Checklist)*

At any time following creation of the PPC2000 Project Partnering Agreement, additional or replacement Partnering Team members can join the Partnering Team by signing Joining Agreements. These should be based on the form set out in PPC2000 Appendix 2, and should state the agreed works or services and agreed payment terms of the Joining Party. They should be signed by the Joining Party and all other Partnering Team members.

Joining Parties could include an additional Consultant or an additional Specialist sub-consultant, sub-contractor or supplier. They could also include a replacement Partnering Team member if one drops out, for example by reason of insolvency or termination for breach in accordance with clause 26 of the Partnering Terms. A Joining Agreement can be signed up at any stage during the pre-construction phase or construction phase of the Project, provided that the PPC2000 Project Partnering Agreement is already in place *(see also clauses 10.2 and 26.9 of the Partnering Terms).*

4.5 PRE-POSSESSION AGREEMENT
(See also Appendix 3 Pre-Possession Agreement Checklist)

At any time following creation of the PPC2000 Project Partnering Agreement, if early work is required on or off Site prior to unconditional approval for commencement of the Project on Site, the Client and the Constructor can sign a Pre-Possession Agreement, based on the form set out in PPC2000 Appendix 3 Part 1. This should state the work agreed, the timetable within which it is to be completed and the price to be paid. PPC2000 makes clear that a Pre-Possession Agreement is not an unconditional commitment to the Project proceeding, that it is governed by all relevant terms of PPC2000 and that the Constructor must cease all Pre-Possession Activities and vacate the Site if and when so requested by the Client Representative. Thus, the Partnering Team can achieve early start of key activities on or off Site and can avoid the use of a *"letter of intent",* with all the contractual uncertainties that such a document often involves *(see also clauses 13.3 and 13.4 of the Partnering Terms).*

4.6   COMMENCEMENT AGREEMENT   *(See also Appendix 10, Flowcharts A and B, and Appendix 4 Commencement Agreement Checklist)*

Once the Partnering Team members have fulfilled the agreed pre-conditions for the Project to proceed on Site *(as set out in clause 14.1 of the Partnering Terms and in the Project Brief)*, they sign a form of Commencement Agreement, based on the form set out in PPC2000 Appendix 3 Part 2. For this purpose, the Client and other Partnering Team members will need to be satisfied that the pre-conditions set out in clause 14 of the Partnering Terms, and any further pre-conditions set out in the Project Brief, have been satisfied. These include agreement of an Agreed Maximum Price and development of sufficient agreed designs, supply chain packages and price details to establish an acceptable level of design and price certainty in the Project Proposals and Price Framework. They also include the agreement of a Project Timetable to govern implementation of the Project on Site, the final agreement of KPIs, targets and incentives and the satisfaction of other pre-conditions such as Site acquisition or funding, grant of planning consent and development of a *"Health and Safety Plan"*.

The Commencement Agreement includes express confirmation by all Partnering Team members that *"To the best of their knowledge the Project is ready to commence on Site"*. It is important that all parties accept this duty to confirm when the Project is ready to commence on Site, and otherwise to notify the remainder of the Partnering Team as to why they believe this is not the case.

In order to agree the basis on which the Commencement Agreement will be signed, PPC2000 requires the Client to identify to other Partnering Team members, at the time of signing the Project Partnering Agreement, all pre-conditions of which it is aware to the Project proceeding on Site. These should be set out in the Project Brief. By this means other Partnering Team members can make a judgement as to the activities required and the obstacles to overcome in order for the Project to proceed on Site. This in turn will help Partnering Team members agree the level of speculative works and services that they are willing to undertake, and the extent to which they need to be reimbursed in respect of abortive costs if any pre-condition is not satisfied and the Project does not proceed on Site.

At any time prior to signature of the Commencement Agreement clause 26.1 of the Partnering Terms entitles the Client to terminate the appointment of all other Partnering Team members if any of the stated pre-conditions are not satisfied or if for any other reason not reasonably foreseeable by the Client it no longer wishes to proceed with the Project. It would be unreasonable to expect a Client to sign an unconditional commitment to a Project that, at the time of signing the Project Partnering Agreement, has not been fully designed or costed. If the Client exercises this right of termination, it will be obliged to pay other Partnering Team members the amounts agreed in respect of approved activities already undertaken, but will not be liable for any other amount.

Once the Commencement Agreement has been signed, all Partnering Team members are committed to their respective roles and responsibilities in carrying out and completing the Project. Rights of termination arise only in respect of insolvency or breach or frustration, subject in the second and third cases to stated periods of notice and procedures including prior Consultation with the Core Group *(see clause 26 of the Partnering Terms)*.

During the period from the Commencement Agreement through to Project Completion, the Constructor assumes primary responsibility for carrying out and completing the Project, subject to Change and agreed treatment of risks, and with input as agreed from other Partnering Team members, in consideration for which the Client agrees to pay the Agreed Maximum Price subject only to agreed adjustments *(see clauses 12, 13, 17 and 18 of the Partnering Terms)*. There is provision under PPC2000 for outstanding designs, supply chain packages and prices to continue to be finalised and agreed during the construction phase - to the extent that these have not already been finalised prior to start on Site *(see clauses 8, 10 and 12 of the Partnering Terms)*. There is also scope for further members to join the Partnering Team under additional Joining Agreements *(see clause 10.2 of the Partnering Terms)*.

Partnered processes continue under PPC2000 after start on Site, including agreed risk sharing, operation of the Early Warning system, agreed activities of the Core Group, and advance evaluation of Changes and events of delay and disruption. Performance of Partnering Team members is assessed against agreed KPI targets, with provision for incentives to reward recognised achievements.

All activities during the construction phase of the Project, where they involve any interface between Partnering Team members, should be agreed to be undertaken within the timescales set out in the Partnering Terms and the Project Timetable, and by stated members of the Partnering Team and Design Team as appropriate.

4.7 POST-PROJECT COMPLETION

"Project Completion" under PPC2000 is defined in PPC2000 Appendix 1 as *"completion of the Project in accordance with the Partnering Documents necessary for the Client to use and occupy the Project to the agreed standards"*. Following Project Completion, the liability of the Partnering Team members is subject to an agreed warranty, an agreed *"Defects Liability Period"* and agreed period of limitations *(see clauses 21, 22 and 27.8 of the Partnering Terms)*. There is also provision for a post-Project Completion review *(see clause 23.6 of the Partnering Terms)*.

CHAPTER 5 - PARTNERING DOCUMENTS

5.1 WHAT ARE THE PARTNERING DOCUMENTS?

PPC2000 condenses into a single contract the complex web of two-party contracts that would otherwise be needed to describe the relationships between the members of the Partnering Team.

The documents supporting PPC2000 (the *"Partnering Documents"*) reflect in almost all cases the equivalent documents required to support any other set of contracts. PPC2000 gives contractual status to three additional documents necessary to integrate and measure the progress of each Partnering Team member's performance, namely the Partnering Timetable, the Project Timetable and the KPIs.

The full set of Partnering Documents forming part of the PPC2000 Partnering Contract comprise the following:-

- The Project Partnering Agreement (described in Chapter 4);

- The Partnering Terms (described in Chapter 6);

- Any Joining Agreements (described in Chapter 4);

- Any Pre-Possession Agreement (described in Chapter 4);

- The Commencement Agreement (described in Chapter 4);

- Any Partnering Charter (described in Chapter 2);

- The Project Brief;

- The Project Proposals;

- The Price Framework;

- The Consultant Services Schedules;

- The Consultant Payment Terms;

- The KPIs.

As stated, certain of the Partnering Documents are described in other chapters of this guide. As to the remaining Partnering Documents, the basic components to be expected in each of them are described below. In each case, these are annotated with cross-references to the relevant clauses of the Partnering Terms.

5.2 PROJECT BRIEF

The Project Brief describes the Client's requirements for the Project, in prescriptive terms if and to the extent that such requirements are already fully established, or in performance terms in order to obtain maximum contributions in the responses and contributions from other Partnering Team members. The essential components of the Project Brief comprise a description of the following:-

- The Project and the Site, including all available information relating to either (clause 1.1);

- The Client's expectations as to the roles, expertise and responsibilities of the Client, the Constructor, Consultants and any Specialists either appointed direct by the Client or required to be appointed by the Constructor, including a section dealing with the Client's expected conduct of Partnering Team members on and off Site (clauses 1.3, 1.5 and 1.6);

- The Client's requirements or proposals as to methods of communication (clause 3.2);

- Confirmation of any Interested Parties and their proposed involvement (clause 3.9);

- Any Client requirements or proposals for secondments, office sharing arrangements and access to computer networks and databases (clause 3.10);

- The Client's requirements or proposals as to record-keeping and arrangements for inspection of activities and records (clause 3.11);

- The Client's objectives for the Project (clause 4);

- Any known constraints on Site possession and access (clause 6.4);

- The Client's required or proposed standards of health and safety and Site welfare (clause 7.2);

- Any required restrictions on removal or replacement of any individual representing any Partnering Team member (clause 7.3);

- The Client's required or proposed employment and training initiatives (clause 7.6);

- Any known designs and design expectations, including the results of any previous Site surveys and investigations (clauses 8.2, 8.3 and 8.6);

- Any Client Volume Supply Agreements (clause 11.1);

- The Client's requirements or proposals for incentives (clause 13.1);

- Any pre-conditions to implementation of the Project on Site additional to those set out in clause 14.1 (clause 14.1(x));

- The Client's required or proposed types and standards of materials, goods and equipment (clause 16.2);

- The Client's required or proposed Quality Management System (clause 16.3);

- The Client's required or proposed measures to deal with Environmental Risk (clause 16.4);

- Any required or proposed security by way of advance payment guarantee, performance bond, parent company guarantee or retention bond (Clause 19.9);

- Any variation to the period of notice prior to Project Completion, details of the Client's required attendance, inspection and testing procedures at Project Completion and any exclusions, pre-conditions and procedures relevant to Project Completion (clause 21.1);

- Any required or proposed Specialist warranties (clause 22.3).

5.3 PROJECT PROPOSALS

The Project Proposals comprise the responses submitted by the Constructor, and possibly also by Consultants and Specialists who are Partnering Team members, to each of the matters comprising the Project Brief.

Where the Client's requirements in the Project Brief are prescriptive, the Project Proposals can comprise a straightforward agreement to implement the stated requirements. Where the Client's requirements in the Project Brief are non-prescriptive, the Project Proposals can comprise detailed submissions by way of all or any of the following:-

- Drawings and specifications;

- Ideas and methods for Value Engineering, Value Management and Risk Management;

- Ideas for cost savings and added value, including suggestions for related incentives;

- Suggestions for improved implementation of other Project partnering processes;

- Proposed roles and responsibilities for Specialist sub-consultants, sub-contractors and suppliers;

- Responses to all and any of the requirements and proposals set out in the Project Brief.

The Project Proposals will be developed during the pre-construction phase, and possibly also during the construction phase, as designs are approved by the Client and incorporated to form part of the Project Proposals (clause 8.12) and as otherwise agreed by the Partnering Team members.

5.4 PRICE FRAMEWORK

The components of the Price Framework as at the date of the Project Partnering Agreement should comprise the following:-

- Agreed amounts payable for Constructor's Services (clause 12.1);

- The Client's Budget for the Project (if known) (clause 12.3);

- The Constructor's agreed Profit (clause 12.4);

- The Constructor's agreed Central Office Overheads (clause 12.4);

- The Constructor's agreed Site Overheads (if known), with a breakdown to facilitate the operation of clause 18.5 (clause 12.4);

- Any known costs in respect of fully designed items or other matters in respect of which fixed prices are agreed at the date of the Project Partnering Agreement (clauses 12.6 and 12.7);

- Any agreed arrangements for discounts or other benefits payable by any Specialists to the Constructor (clause 12.8);

- The Constructor's statement as to its proposed pricing of risks, including any prospective risk contingencies (clause 12.9);

- Any agreed payment milestones, activity schedules or cashflows, or other agreed payment arrangements or payment intervals (amending clause 20.2);

- Any agreed periods for payment (if revising those set out in any of clauses 20.3, 20.4, 20.14 and 20.15);

- Any agreed fluctuation provisions (clause 20.10).

The Price Framework will be built up in agreed stages according to the approval of Business Cases for Direct Labour Packages and Preferred Specialists, the approval of tenders submitted by other Specialists (clauses 12.6 and 12.7), the approval of Value Engineering and Value Management exercises (clause 5.1(iii)) and the agreed treatment of risk (clause 12.9). In each case these will establish pricing to a level of detail approved by the Client Representative, and the relevant financial information will be incorporated to form part of the Price Framework.

5.5 CONSULTANT SERVICES SCHEDULES

Each Consultant should have its role, expertise and responsibilities described in sufficient detail in a *"Consultant Services Schedule"* that is integrated with the other Consultant Services Schedules, and also with the Project Brief and Project Proposals, in order to identify the interfaces between all Partnering Team members.

For design Consultants, the agreed services should follow the stages of the PPC2000 design development process (clause 8) subject to agreed amendments.

For the *"Lead Designer"*, if this is a Consultant, the agreed services should clarify all those responsibilities set out in clause 8 and the working relationships between the Lead Designer and other members of the Design Team.

For cost Consultants, the agreed services should include provision of updated cost estimates at each stage of design development (clause 8.7) and should include appropriate input at each stage of supply chain development (clause 10), review of *"Volume Supply Agreements"* (clause 11), development of prices (clause 12) and agreement and implementation of financial incentives (clause 13). They should also include appropriate input to the agreed procedures for Change (clause 17), risk management (clause 18) and payment (clause 20).

For the Client Representative, the agreed services should include clarification of all the agreed functions described in the PPC2000 Partnering Terms *(see also Appendix 6 Client Representative Checklist)*.

For the *"Planning Supervisor"*, the agreed services should include details describing the role identified in clauses 7.1 and 8.9 of the PPC2000 Partnering Terms.

In all cases, advice on the content and integration of the Consultant Services Schedules should be obtained from the Partnering Adviser.

The detail of the Consultant Services Schedule of each Consultant will depend on the nature of the Project and the particular responsibilities that each accepts. As regards design Consultants, it will also depend on the corresponding design responsibilities accepted by the Constructor and Specialists. Where design Consultants are appointed prior to Specialists working in the same field (for example a mechanical and electrical services Consultant appointed in advance of the selection of mechanical and electrical Specialists), it is advisable to leave sufficient flexibility in any relevant Consultant Services Schedule to allow, for example, an increased design responsibility to be taken on by the relevant Specialist when selected, if this is agreed to be in the best interests of the Project.

In all cases, the Consultant Services Schedules should specify the individuals comprising each Consultant's own team and any agreed constraints on their removal or replacement (clause 7.3), should describe the other resources agreed to be deployed by each Consultant and should state each Consultant's commitment to attend meetings of the Partnering Team members, Core Group members and Design Team members as appropriate. They should also state each Consultant's agreement to participate in Value Engineering, Value Management and Risk Management exercises, and in partnering workshops as appropriate.

In all respects, the Consultant Services Schedules should be consistent and integrated with each other and with the Project Brief and Project Proposals. They should also be fully integrated with the Partnering Timetable and Project Timetable.

5.6 CONSULTANT PAYMENT TERMS

The *"Consultant Payment Terms"* for each Consultant state the fees and expenses payable to them for performance of their agreed services in connection with the Project, and should cover all and any financial entitlements.

The Consultant Payment Terms should also state any agreed payment milestones, activity schedules or cashflows and any other payment arrangements or agreed payment intervals (clause 20.2) and any revisions to the standard PPC2000 periods for payment of Consultants (clause 20.4). They should also state any agreed fluctuation arrangements (clause 20.10).

5.7 PARTNERING TIMETABLE

The Partnering Timetable states the agreed activities of each Partnering Team member during the pre-construction phase of the Project. It should include each of the following, identifying each interface between Partnering Team members:-

- Agreed dates for Core Group and Partnering Team meetings (clauses 3.5 and 3.8);

- Agreed dates for Value Engineering, Value Management and Risk Management exercises (clause 5.1(iii));

- Agreed dates for partnering workshops (clause 5.1(iv));

- Finalisation of the Project Timetable (clause 6.2);

- Development of a Health and Safety Plan (clause 7.1);

- Completion of pre-commencement Site surveys and investigations (clause 8.4);

- Development of an integrated design, supply and construction process and grant of any required planning permission and other pre-commencement regulatory approvals (clause 8);

- Agreed dates for Design Team meetings (clause 8.13);

- Build-up of the supply chain (clause 10);

- Build-up of prices and finalisation of an Agreed Maximum Price supported by a Price Framework (clause 12);

- Finalisation of incentives (clause 13) and of KPIs and targets (clause 23);

- Satisfaction of all other pre-conditions stated in clause 14.1 and in the Project Brief.

The Partnering Timetable should also identify matters agreed to be outside the control of Partnering Team members that could obstruct or otherwise delay subsequent agreed activities.

Every activity stated in the Partnering Timetable should also state the named Partnering Team member responsible for it.

5.8 PROJECT TIMETABLE

The Project Timetable states the agreed activities of each Partnering Team member during the construction phase of the Project, if and to the extent that these involve interface between Partnering Team members, and should clearly identify each such interface. It should include the following:-

- Agreed dates for Core Group and Partnering Team meetings (clauses 3.5 and 3.8);

- Agreed dates for Value Engineering, Value Management and Risk Management exercises (clause 5.1(iii));

- Agreed dates for partnering workshops (clause 5.1(iv));

- Constraints on Site possession and/or access (clauses 6.4 and 15.3(i));

- Further development and finalisation of an integrated design, supply and construction process (clause 8);

- Agreed dates for Design Team meetings (clause 8.13);

- Finalisation of the selection of any remaining Specialists (clause 10);

- Finalisation of any provisional sums and other outstanding elements of the Agreed Maximum Price (clause 12);

- Review of progress against KPIs and targets (clause 23);

- Agreed date for post-Project Completion review (clause 23.6).

The Project Timetable should also identify matters agreed to be outside the control of Partnering Team members that could obstruct or otherwise delay subsequent agreed activities.

Every activity stated in the Project Timetable should also state the named Partnering Team member responsible for it.

5.9 KEY PERFORMANCE INDICATORS

KPIs should be agreed, at least provisionally, at the time of signing the Project Partnering Agreement, and should be finalised prior to signing the Commencement Agreement (clause 23.1). They should include the following:-

- The agreed KPIs themselves using as a starting point those KPIs listed in clause 4.2, adjusted (whether by addition or reduction) to reflect a set of KPIs that are manageable by the Partnering Team and relevant to their agreed priorities and objectives;

- Agreed targets for performance of Partnering Team members by reference to the agreed KPIs;

- Agreed measures to remedy any failure to achieve any of the targets set out in the KPIs, to the extent that this is not left for later Core Group agreement (clause 23.2);

- Links between payment of the Constructor or any Consultant or Specialist and achievement of any of the targets stated in the KPIs (clause 13.5), by way of incentives to reward Partnering Team members who meet or exceed their agreed KPI targets or by way of remedies for failure to achieve such targets (clauses 13.5 and 23.2).

CHAPTER 6 - PPC2000 PARTNERING TERMS - CLAUSE BY CLAUSE

CLAUSE 1   **PROJECT & PARTNERING TEAM MEMBERS**

Introduction   Clause 1 deals with identification of the Project and the Site, the identities and status of the Partnering Team members, the Definitions used in PPC2000 and the key values underpinning the relationships between Partnering Team members.

Clause 1.1   states that the Partnering Contract relates to the Project and the Site as identified in the Project Partnering Agreement and is made between the Client, the Constructor and the other parties who have executed the Project Partnering Agreement.

     The Client and the Constructor will be identified by insertion of relevant details against those titles at the end of the Project Partnering Agreement. The nature of the Project and the Site will be stated briefly at the beginning of the Project Partnering Agreement, and will be further described in the Project Brief and Project Proposals.

Clause 1.2   states that the members of the Partnering Team are the parties who are signatories to the Project Partnering Agreement, subject to change in accordance with the Partnering Terms and subject to addition where Joining Agreements are executed in accordance with clause 10.2 or clause 26.9.

Clause 1.3   states the central principle of the PPC2000 Partnering Contract, namely that Partnering Team members *"shall work together and individually in the spirit of trust, fairness and mutual co-operation for the benefit of the Project"*. It clarifies this principle with a qualification that appears repeatedly in PPC2000, namely that the obligations of the Partnering Team members are those that fall *"within the scope of their agreed roles, expertise and responsibilities as stated in the Partnering Documents"*. This qualification clarifies that no Partnering Team member is accepting obligations beyond its agreed competence and experience.

Clause 1.4   provides that words and expressions are defined as set out in Appendix 1 or, if not in conflict with Appendix 1, as stated elsewhere in the Partnering Documents.

Clause 1.5   describes the status of Consultants, who comprise the Client Representative and any other party providing design or other services to the Client, whether or not they are Partnering Team members. All Consultants are paid by the Client in accordance with Consultant Payment Terms and provide services described in Consultant Services Schedules.

     Those Consultants who are or will become Partnering Team members should be listed in the appropriate section of the Project Partnering Agreement, with reference to their names and professional disciplines, or with reference only to their professional disciplines if specific organisations have not yet been identified.

     The Consultant Payment Terms and Consultant Services Schedules for each Consultant who is a Partnering Team member should be clearly identified, and should be signed as Partnering Documents by all Partnering Team members *(see also Chapters 5.5 and 5.6)*.

     Those Consultants who are Partnering Team members will be further identified by the insertion of relevant details against their respective titles at the end of the Project Partnering Agreement or in any relevant Joining Agreement.

Clause 1.6 describes the status of Specialists, who comprise all parties providing works or services or supplies to the Constructor (although note the exception of Specialists appointed directly by the Client under clause 10.11), whether or not they are Partnering Team members. All such Specialists are paid by the Constructor in accordance with Specialist Payment Terms, to be annexed to the Project Partnering Agreement or a Joining Agreement under which a Specialist becomes a member of the Partnering Team or set out in the relevant Specialist Contract entered into between the Constructor and each such Specialist *(see also Chapter 7)*.

Those Specialists who are or will become Partnering Team members should be listed in the appropriate section of the Project Partnering Agreement with reference to their names and professional disciplines/trades, or with reference only to their professional disciplines/trades if specific organisations have not yet been identified.

Those Specialists who are Partnering Team members will be further identified by the insertion of relevant details against their respective titles at the end of the Project Partnering Agreement or any relevant Joining Agreement.

Clause 1.7 states that all Partnering Team members shall act reasonably and without delay in all matters governed by the Partnering Contract.

CLAUSE 2   PARTNERING DOCUMENTS

Introduction It is important that all Partnering Documents which form part of the Partnering Contract at the time when the Project Partnering Agreement is entered into are clearly identified and signed by all Partnering Team members. Certain of these documents can be annexed to the Project Partnering Agreement, for example the Partnering Timetable, the Consultant Services Schedules, the Consultant Payment Terms and the KPIs. This is entirely a matter of what is most practical.

However, those Partnering Documents that it is not practical to annex to the Project Partnering Agreement, which are likely to comprise the Project Brief, the Project Proposals and the Price Framework, need to be clearly identified using those headings and signed simultaneously with the Project Partnering Agreement *(see also Chapter 5 and Appendix 1 Project Partnering Agreement Checklist)*.

Clause 2.1 states that the roles, expertise and responsibilities of the Partnering Team members are as set out in the Partnering Documents, which govern the relationships between them and the implementation of the Project.

Clause 2.2 sets out the list of Partnering Documents and provides for additional or amended Partnering Documents to be developed in accordance with the Partnering Terms. These can include any Partnering Charter (clause 5.6), the Project Timetable (clause 6), designs approved as Project Proposals (clause 8), prices incorporated in the Price Framework (clause 12), Joining Agreements (clause 10.2 or clause 26.9), any Pre-Possession Agreement (clause 13.3) and any Commencement Agreement (clause 15.1).

Clause 2.3 provides that any Partnering Document created or amended in accordance with PPC2000 shall be binding on all Partnering Team members, but shall not create or amend any role, expertise, responsibilities or other obligations of any Partnering Team member who does not sign it.

Clause 2.4	sets out the principle that each Partnering Team member who prepares or contributes to any Partnering Document shall be responsible for the consequences of any error, omission in, or any discrepancy between, the Partnering Documents that it prepares or in its contributions to them. A Partnering Team member can qualify that responsibility to the extent that in such Partnering Documents it states its reliance on any contribution or information provided by any other Partnering Team members.
Clause 2.5	states that Partnering Documents are complementary, and requires Partnering Team members to warn each other of any error, omission or discrepancy and (within their agreed roles, expertise and responsibilities) to put forward proposals to resolve it fairly and constructively within the Partnering Team without adversely affecting cost or time or quality. These proposals are for Client approval after Core Group *"Consultation"*.
Clause 2.6	establishes an order of priority of Partnering Documents, to be applied if any discrepancy is not resolved by agreement and unless a different order is agreed by all Partnering Team members.

CLAUSE 3   COMMUNICATION AND ORGANISATION

Introduction	Clause 3 deals with communication and organisation between Partnering Team members in order to *"organise and integrate their activities as a collaborative team"*. Most significantly, it deals with the creation of the Core Group, the individuals who working together will determine the extent to which partnering adds value to the Project process. These individuals need to be carefully chosen, for example in terms of their level of seniority, their knowledge of the Project and their relationships with other Core Group members. It is important that Core Group members understand their functions and responsibilities, and that they have the experience and temperament necessary for them to identify solutions that will benefit the Project and the Partnering Team as a whole rather than only the organisation that is their employer.
	It is primarily through the Core Group that the behavioural, cultural and aspirational aspects of Project partnering are connected to the practical integration of Project relationships and processes *(see also Appendix 5 Core Group Checklist)*.
	The Core Group is the medium through which partnering can fulfil its full potential. If the Core Group fail to reach *"Consensus"* on any issue within the scope of their authority, this will be evidence of limitations on, or even failure of, the partnering relationships. In the absence of Core Group Consensus, PPC2000 continues to govern the delivery of the Project, leaving the Partnering Team members to rely on their agreed contractual rights and obligations where the Core Group has not agreed a better solution. If the Core Group repeatedly fails to reach Consensus, Partnering Team members should consider whether all or any of them have sufficiently briefed those of their employees who are Core Group members, and also whether they have selected the right individuals to be Core Group members.
Clause 3.1	establishes the principle of transparent and co-operative exchange of information.
Clause 3.2	states the agreed methods of communication which will apply except where others are agreed in writing. All communications are effective from the date of delivery and all the listed methods are those that create evidence of delivery. Ordinary

post is not stated to be an agreed method of communication because, without an agreed system of acknowledgement, there is no means of evidencing receipt. Email is recognised as an agreed method of communication if the Partnering Team members have signed an appropriate procedural agreement governing its use.

Clause 3.3   describes the Core Group, whose role is *"to review and stimulate the progress of the Project and the implementation of the Partnering Contract"* and to fulfil their agreed functions in accordance with the Partnering Documents.

The Core Group members, who will be named individuals, should be listed in the Project Partnering Agreement along with any agreed arrangements for alternates or substitutes at any stage in the Project partnering process.

Clause 3.4   states the responsibility of Partnering Team members for their employees who are Core Group members.

Clause 3.5   describes the procedure for Core Group meetings. Partnering Team members shall be notified and entitled to attend. It is desirable to attempt to predict the required Core Group meetings in the Partnering Timetable and Project Timetable in order to assist Partnering Team members in agreeing and costing appropriate resources.

Clause 3.6   provides that Core Group decisions are to be *"by Consensus of all Core Group members present at that meeting"*. Consensus is defined as *"unanimous agreement following reasoned discussion"*. If a Core Group member is absent from a meeting, Consensus can be achieved without him or her, so no-one can veto a proposed Core Group decision by non-attendance.

Clause 3.7   establishes a valuable technique for partnered collaboration and risk management, namely the Early Warning system. Each Partnering Team member is required to notify the others as soon as it is aware of any matter adversely affecting or threatening the Project or its own performance, and to include proposals (within its agreed role, expertise and responsibilities) for avoiding or remedying such matter. These are referred to the Core Group to agree a course of action.

The Early Warning System is a key test of whether Partnering Team members have developed sufficient mutual trust and confidence to notify concerns outside their agreed area of competence and experience, and also to notify problems in their own performance. The role of the Core Group in agreeing how to avoid or remedy a matter in respect of which it has been given Early Warning is clearly preferable to such a matter being referred to the decision of one Partnering Team member alone. When operated fairly in the hands of a Core Group that understands its brief, the Early Warning system can be of enormous value to the Partnering Team members and the Project in avoiding an adversarial response to a problem and in mitigating its adverse effects.

Clause 3.8   deals with meetings of the Partnering Team members.

Clause 3.9   recognises the status of *"Interested Parties"*, namely any organisation or group of individuals which has an interest relating to the Project, but is not itself a Partnering Team member. Partnering Team members agree to establish the *"maximum practicable involvement"* of Interested Parties.

Interested Parties could include for example owners, end users, funders or regulators. Arrangements in the Partnering Documents by reference to such Interested Parties should describe the nature of their interest and the extent of their

GUIDE to PPC2000 & SPC2000   © ACA and Trowers & Hamlins 2003

involvement in the Project. Recognition of any Interested Party, by reference to clause 3.9 in the Project Partnering Agreement, does not create a duty of care in its favour. If this is appropriate, it can be achieved by a collateral warranty by reference to clause 22.2, or by operation of the Contracts (Rights of Third Parties) Act 1999 by reference to clause 22.4.

Clause 3.10 provides for consideration and development of secondments, office sharing arrangements and mutual access to data wherever this is of benefit to the Project, subject to agreed constraints of confidentiality (clause 25.5) and appropriate procedural agreements.

Clause 3.11 requires the Partnering Team members to keep records as required by the Partnering Documents and, subject to agreed constraints of confidentiality (clause 25.5), to permit their inspection by other Partnering Team members and agreed third parties.

CLAUSE 4   PARTNERING OBJECTIVES

Introduction This clause summarises the reasons why the Partnering Team members agree to utilise Project partnering to integrate their relationships and activities, and makes express reference to the Egan Report. It states a range of objectives and links these to agreed KPI targets. Partnering Team members should limit the number, type and method of measurement of KPIs to reflect what is of practical value to them. In identifying appropriate KPI targets, it is important that Partnering Team members also state clearly, in the Partnering Document comprising the KPIs, the agreed financial and other consequences (if any) of meeting or exceeding those targets or failing to meet them. This is dealt with further in clauses 13.5 (Payment and KPIs), 23.1 (KPIs) and 24.2 (Strategic Alliancing).

Clause 4.1 provides for partnering objectives *"for the benefit of the Project and for the mutual benefit of Partnering Team members"* that comprise:-

- trust/fairness/mutual co-operation/agreed common goals/mutual understanding of expectations and values;

- finalisation of designs/timetables/prices/supply chain;

- innovation/efficiency/cost-effectiveness/lean production/reduction or elimination of waste;

- completion of the Project to agreed time/price/quality;

- measurable continuous improvement by reference to agreed KPI targets;

- other objectives set out in the Partnering Documents.

Clause 4.2 refers expressly to the recommendations of the Egan Report and links these to the targets stated in the Partnering Team members' agreed KPIs. Additional to the objectives listed in the Egan Report are whole-life costs, improved quality and improved *"Sustainability"*.

CLAUSE 5   CLIENT REPRESENTATIVE AND PARTNERING ADVISER

Introduction

This clause deals with two key roles in driving forward the Project partnering process. The first is the Client Representative who acts as project manager, has authority to represent the Client in all matters other than membership of the Core Group, and also accepts a duty to act fairly and constructively in the exercise of any discretion pursuant to the Partnering Terms. Under specific Partnering Terms, a decision of the Client Representative may be challenged if it is contrary to the Partnering Documents or does not reflect the facts of the relevant issue, and ultimately a disputed decision may be referred for determination in accordance with the agreed mechanisms for problem-solving and avoidance or resolution of disputes under clause 27 *(see also Appendix 6 Client Representative Checklist).*

This clause also deals with the Partnering Adviser, who is an independent adviser offering support and advice to the Partnering Team members (together or individually) as to the partnering process, the development of the partnering relationships and the operation of the Partnering Contract. The Partnering Adviser should draw up the Project Partnering Agreement and other PPC2000 agreements, should review the other Partnering Documents, and should seek to ensure that all Partnering Team members understand fully the commitments, expectations and prospective rewards that the Partnering Contract creates *(see also Chapter 9 and Appendix 7 Partnering Adviser Checklist).*

It is envisaged that the Client Representative should be a Partnering Team member, but (in line with the recommendations of the CIC Guide) that the Partnering Adviser should not be a Partnering Team member.

Clause 5.1

describes the role of the Client Representative and provides that the Client Representative shall:

- exercise *"any discretion fairly and constructively"*;

- *"facilitate·an integrated design, supply and construction process in accordance with the Partnering Documents"*; and

- be supported by *"other Partnering Team members as stated in the Partnering Documents"*.

It also describes a number of specific Client Representative functions including organisation of meetings of the Core Group and Partnering Team, organisation and monitoring of Value Engineering, Value Management and Risk Management exercises, organisation of partnering workshops and monitoring of Project implementation on and off Site. The Client Representative's agreed functions and agreed resources should be clarified in a Consultant Services Schedule *(see also Chapter 5.5).*

Clause 5.2

provides that the Client Representative is authorised to represent the Client in all matters except membership of the Core Group. Any restrictions on this authority need to be set out in the Project Partnering Agreement.

Clause 5.3

authorises the Client Representative to issue instructions to the Constructor *"Where necessary and without prejudicing the collaborative spirit of the partnering relationships"* - including as to *"opening up for inspection or testing of any part of the Project and the rectification or replacement at no cost to the Client of any designs, works, services, materials, goods or equipment that are defective or otherwise not in accordance with the Partnering Documents"*.

GUIDE to PPC2000 & SPC2000   © ACA and Trowers & Hamlins 2003

Clause 5.4   provides a system for the Constructor to object to any instruction of the Client Representative within strict time limits if it is contrary to the Partnering Documents or otherwise demonstrably not in the best interests of the Project, and for a consultative process following any such objection.

Clause 5.5   provides that, subject to the Constructor's right of objection under clause 5.4, the Constructor shall promptly carry out instructions that are consistent with the Partnering Documents. It also provides for a notice system in the event of non-compliance that culminates in the right of the Client to pay another party to carry out an instruction and to recover consequent additional costs from the Constructor.

Clause 5.6   provides for the appointment of a Partnering Adviser, an independent individual who may be called upon to provide advice and support to Partnering Team members, together or individually, subject to prior agreement of his or her costs and duty of care *(see also Chapter 9)*.

The Partnering Adviser's name and address should be stated in the Project Partnering Agreement.

The stated functions of the Partnering Adviser include selection of Partnering Team members, team-building, review of Partnering Documents and Specialist Contracts, preparation of the Project Partnering Agreement and other PPC2000 Agreements, *"provision of fair and constructive advice as to the partnering process, the development of the partnering relationships and the operation of the Partnering Contract"*, attendance at meetings as required by the Core Group and Partnering Team and assistance in solving problems and avoidance or resolution of disputes in accordance with clause 27.

Clause 5.7   provides for replacement of the Partnering Adviser at any time by Core Group decision. It is partly to maintain this flexibility that the Partnering Adviser should not be a Partnering Team member.

CLAUSE 6   PARTNERING TIMETABLE AND PROJECT TIMETABLE

Introduction   PPC2000 goes further than any other standard form contract in programming the agreed activities of the Partnering Team members, during both the pre-construction phase and the construction phase of the Project. It gives contractual status to the Partnering Timetable, dealing with activities prior to commencement on Site, and to the Project Timetable, dealing with activities after commencement on Site.

It is important that these documents are prepared with considerable care and are fully understood by Partnering Team members, as they comprise the spine of the Partnering Contract and should document clearly the extent to which Partnering Team members can expect to rely on each other to meet agreed targets or deadlines. It is also important that these documents identify all and any known pre-conditions, obstacles and other matters outside the control of Partnering Team members which could delay achievement of subsequent targets or deadlines.

Clause 6.1   refers to the Partnering Document known as the Partnering Timetable, prepared in order to govern the activities of Partnering Team members during the period prior to the date of the Commencement Agreement. The Partnering Timetable is a valuable project management tool which offers a unique opportunity for Partnering Team members to agree the timing of their activities and interfaces during the pre-construction phase of the Project. It should state clearly which Partnering

Team members agree to do what during the pre-construction phase, when they agree to do it, and what pre-conditions or obstacles outside the Partnering Team's control (e.g. third party approvals) need to be overcome before proceeding from one activity to the next. The Partnering Timetable should be annexed to the Project Partnering Agreement, and clearly identified as a Partnering Document *(see also Chapter 5.7)*.

Clause 6.2   provides for development of the Project Timetable, governing activities after the date of the Commencement Agreement, to be prepared by the Constructor for Core Group review and Client approval. The Project Timetable should be annexed to the Commencement Agreement, and clearly identified as a Partnering Document *(see also Chapter 5.8)*.

The Project Timetable should not give contractual status to matters that are entirely within the Constructor's control. It should cover only the agreed Date of Possession and Date for Completion, any agreed Sections and all required interfaces between Partnering Team members during the construction phase, for example completion and approval of outstanding design details, procurement and approval of outstanding services/works packages, and arrangements for access to and possession of all or part of the Site.

Clause 6.3   provides that the Partnering Timetable or Project Timetable may divide the Project into Sections, in which case all relevant references in the Partnering Contract will apply to each and any Section as well as to the Project as a whole.

Clause 6.4   recognises that Site possession and access may be subject to constraints and procedures set out in the Commencement Agreement and the Project Timetable. Confirmation as to any parts of the Site in exclusive or non-exclusive possession should be stated in the Commencement Agreement, as should any constraints on Site possession/access and any arrangements for deferred or interrupted Site possession.

Clause 6.5   requires compliance with the Project Timetable as agreed, subject to acceleration or postponement (clause 6.6), Change (clause 17), agreed risk events (clause 18), suspension for non-payment (clause 20.17) and suspension or abandonment of the Project (clause 26.6).

Clause 6.6   allows for the Client Representative to instruct acceleration, postponement or resequencing of any date/period in the Project Timetable and provides for this to be treated as a Change.

Clause 6.7   provides for the Constructor to prepare and circulate regular updates to the Project Timetable, and states that receipt or use of any such update shall not be evidence of a Partnering Team member's agreement to its contents.

CLAUSE 7   **HEALTH AND SAFETY, SITE WELFARE AND EMPLOYEES**

Introduction   This clause deals with firstly health and safety and site welfare obligations, and secondly responsibility for individuals employed by or under the authority of Partnering Team members. It encourages health and safety and Site welfare measures as well as employment and training initiatives beyond the scope of basic legal obligations, but creates obligations beyond those legal obligations only to the extent that these are described specifically in the Partnering Documents.

Clause 7.1   creates contractual commitments in respect of the statutory obligations of the relevant Partnering Team members under the CDM Regulations. The development of a Health and Safety Plan is a pre-condition under clause 14.1 to the signature of the Commencement Agreement and the Project commencing on Site.

Clause 7.2   requires Partnering Team members to work together and individually, within their agreed roles, expertise and responsibilities, to achieve *"the highest possible standards of health and safety"* in relation to the Project. Any such agreed standards are to be described in the Partnering Documents.

Clause 7.3   requires Partnering Team members to employ individuals who have the necessary skills, qualifications and experience. Any constraint on the removal or replacement of an individual employed by any Partnering Team member needs to be stated in the Partnering Documents.

Clause 7.4   states the responsibility of Partnering Team members for their employees and other individuals under their control.

Clause 7.5   entitles the Client to require, after Core Group Consultation, exclusion of any individual from the Project and the Site.

Clause 7.6   provides for implementation of agreed employment and training initiatives as described in the Partnering Documents or as otherwise agreed.

CLAUSE 8   **DESIGN AND PROCESS DEVELOPMENT** *(See also Appendix 10 Flowchart C)*

Introduction   This clause describes the structured, collaborative design and process development facilitated under PPC2000 through the early appointment of the design Consultants and the Constructor, and through the early selection of Specialists. Specific design roles, expertise and responsibilities of each Partnering Team member should be stated in the Project Brief, the Project Proposals and the Consultant Services Schedules, with the timing of key activities and interfaces set out in the Partnering Timetable and Project Timetable. It is important to note that responsibility for design co-ordination rests with the agreed Lead Designer and that the contributions of each Design Team member under clause 8 will also be governed by clause 2.4 (whereby the party that prepares or contributes to any Partnering Document shall be responsible for the consequences of any error or omission in, or any discrepancy between, such Partnering Documents or its contributions to them). In order to clarify the scope of their contributions to design, later Partnering Team members signing Joining Agreements should state (by reference to clause 2.4) any specific reliance on any contribution or information provided by other Partnering Team members whose designs form the starting point for their work or create assumptions upon which they rely.

Clause 8 recognises the importance of Value Engineering exercises at appropriate points in the design development process, and these should be identified in the Partnering Timetable and the Project Timetable. There is also the requirement for Design Team members to take into account the Client's Budget and to obtain and provide updated cost estimates with all design submissions: this will require regular collaboration between the Design Team and the appointed cost Consultant.

Clause 8.1   provides for design and process development by the Lead Designer and other Design Team members, with the objective of achieving best value for the Client.

The identity of the Lead Designer should be stated in the Project Partnering Agreement, as should any agreed change in the party fulfilling that role at any point during the Project partnering process.

The members of the Design Team should be listed in the Project Partnering Agreement. If all Design Team members have not been identified at the point of signing the Project Partnering Agreement, then the list should state their relevant professional disciplines/trades and confirm whether they will be Consultants or Specialists.

Clause 8.2   provides for agreed design contributions of the Design Team members and establishes the role and authority of the Lead Designer to co-ordinate those contributions.

Clause 8.3   provides for a process governing design during the pre-construction phase, including preparation of outline designs and alternative solutions; development of those designs with maximum Specialist input; and finalisation of detailed designs sufficient to select Specialists, develop the Price Framework and obtain any required regulatory approvals, subject to Core Group Consultation and Client approval at each stage, all within the periods stated in the Partnering Timetable *(See also Appendix 10 Flowchart C)*. Any amendment to this design development process should be clearly described in the Project Partnering Agreement, the Project Brief, the Project Proposals and the Consultant Services Schedules.

Clause 8.4   provides for the commissioning and undertaking of any required Site surveys and investigations and for the Lead Designer and Design Team to review their results, to advise the Client and Core Group as to their effect and to amend the designs as required for Core Group Consultation and Client approval. There should be listed in the Project Partnering Agreement all and any Site surveys and investigations that remain to be undertaken, together with the names of the Partnering Team members responsible for commissioning or undertaking them. These activities should be linked to the agreed process for risk analysis and risk management, set out elsewhere in the Partnering Documents.

Clause 8.5   provides for the Lead Designer, with agreed Partnering Team input, to pursue all regulatory approvals and report to the Client and Core Group with recommendations to overcome any problems.

Clause 8.6   provides for the continuation of the design process after the Commencement Agreement, for preparation and submission of designs by Design Team members, for review by recipients, for appropriate contributions and for Lead Designer co-ordination, all within the periods stated in the Project Timetable *(See also Appendix 10 Flowchart C)*. Any amendment to this design development process should be clearly described in the Project Partnering Agreement, the Project Brief, the Project Proposals and the Consultant Services Schedules.

Clause 8.7   requires that, at each stage of design development, the Lead Designer and Design Team shall take into account the Client's Budget and obtain and provide updated cost estimates.

Clause 8.8   provides for designs to be amended as necessary to adopt the results of Value Engineering exercises, where these are approved by the Client after Core Group Consultation.

Clause 8.9   provides for designs to be copied to the Planning Supervisor at each stage, for advice on health and safety implications as appropriate.

Clause 8.10   states that no approval or comment on any design affects the responsibility of the party preparing or contributing to it.

Clause 8.11   provides a system for the Constructor to object to any design within strict time limits, if neither the Constructor nor any Specialist has prepared or contributed to it, and if it is contrary to the Partnering Documents or otherwise demonstrably not in the best interests of the Project, and describes a consultative process following any such objection.

Clause 8.12   provides for approved designs to become part of the Project Proposals. The developed set of such Project Proposals should be identified in the Commencement Agreement and should be signed as agreed Partnering Documents at the time of entering into the Commencement Agreement *(See also Chapter 5 and Appendix 4 Commencement Agreement Checklist)*.

Clause 8.13   provides for the Lead Designer to arrange, and for Design Team members to attend, Design Team meetings. It is desirable to attempt to predict the required Design Team meetings in the Partnering Timetable and Project Timetable, in order to assist Partnering Team members in agreeing and costing appropriate resources.

CLAUSE 9   INTELLECTUAL PROPERTY

Introduction   The warranty, indemnity and licence established by this clause are mutual obligations of all Partnering Team members, including the Client as well as the Constructor, Consultants and Specialists. The clause recognises the importance to the originator of the Intellectual Property Rights in any design or document, and the need for these to be licensed for all appropriate purposes relating to the Project, for liability to be restricted to agreed purposes, and for ownership of documents and other embodiments of designs to transfer to the Client in the event of breach or insolvency.

Clause 9.1   establishes a mutual warranty and indemnity in respect of infringement of Intellectual Property Rights.

Clause 9.2   sets out a mutual licence to copy and use designs and other documents for the completion of the Project (and for the Client to operate the Project), with a right to transfer and sub-license for the same purposes.

Clause 9.3   limits liability for designs and documents to the purposes for which it was agreed they would be prepared.

Clause 9.4   transfers ownership in documents and other physical embodiments of designs to the Client in the event that the appointment of the Partnering Team member who produced such designs or documents is terminated for breach or insolvency.

CLAUSE 10   SUPPLY CHAIN *(See also Appendix 10 Flowchart D)*

Introduction   This clause describes a process which encourages selection and appointment of Specialist sub-consultants, sub-contractors and suppliers at the earliest opportunity. It also provides for the establishment of relationships with these parties that are complementary to those described in the Partnering Contract and, where appropriate, for Specialists to become Partnering Team members by signing Joining Agreements. The clause recognises the potential for agreeing single source appointment of Preferred Specialists and for the Constructor to use its own resources pursuant to Direct Labour Packages. However, where best value cannot be established on such a basis in a Business Case submitted by the Constructor, the clause provides for competitive open-book selection of appropriate Specialists through a process monitored by the Client Representative.

Clause 10.1   records the agreement to establish relationships with Specialist sub-consultants, sub-contractors and suppliers that are open-book to the maximum achievable extent; that reflect the Client's requirements, the interests of Partnering Team members and the needs of the Project; that secure the best available warranties and support; that maximise the potential for Specialist innovation and other contributions; that establish and demonstrate best value; and that establish, wherever possible, complementary partnering relationships.

Clause 10.2   sets out the procedure for certain Specialists to become Partnering Team members by executing Joining Agreements based on the form set out in PPC2000 Appendix 2 *(see also Chapter 4.4 and Appendix 2 Joining Agreement Checklist)*.

Clause 10.3   provides for instances where the Constructor wishes to submit a single-source Business Case for Client approval, in respect of either a Direct Labour Package or a Preferred Specialist.

Clause 10.4   provides for analysis of any such Business Case by the Client and Core Group, and for the Constructor's responsibility to demonstrate best value.

Clause 10.5   entitles the Client, after Core Group Consultation, to require market testing of any Business Case with which it is not satisfied.

Clause 10.6   provides for a tender process in respect of prospective Specialists (except where a Direct Labour Package or Preferred Specialist is approved), and for selection on the basis of best value, including experience of partnering and proposals for achieving agreed KPI targets.

Clause 10.7   deals with the treatment of tender returns and other documents during a Specialist tender process, and the monitoring role of the Client Representative in all Specialist tenders and related interviews/meetings.

Clause 10.8   emphasises the requirement to encourage maximum Specialist contributions to and participation in an integrated design, supply and construction process.

Clause 10.9   requires Client approval of any proposed *"Specialist Contract"*.

Clause 10.10   recognises that Consultants may become Specialists.

Clause 10.11   recognises that the Client may appoint certain Specialists direct, whether or not they are later novated to the Constructor. The role of any Specialist to be appointed direct by the Client should be clearly described in the Project Partnering Agreement, by reference to its professional discipline/trade if a specific organisation has not yet been identified.

Clause 10.12   provides for Constructor responsibility in respect of Specialist performance (except Specialists appointed direct by the Client under clause 10.11).

Clause 10.13   requires Client Consultation prior to Constructor termination of any Specialist Contract, and Client approval after Core Group Consultation prior to appointment of any replacement Specialist.

GUIDE to PPC2000 & SPC2000 © ACA and Trowers & Hamlins 2003

Clause 10.14   provides that only the Constructor has authority to issue instructions to Specialists (except Specialists appointed direct by the Client under clause 10.11).

CLAUSE 11   VOLUME SUPPLY AGREEMENTS

Introduction   It may be that particular Partnering Team members will have access to volume supply arrangements offering preferential terms, that can be introduced to the other Partnering Team members for the benefit of the Project. This clause describes how such arrangements should be considered and adopted by the Partnering Team.

Clause 11.1   provides that any Partnering Team member shall notify the Client Representative of any Volume Supply Agreement that could benefit the Project, namely any agreement offering preferential terms for the supply of materials, goods or equipment.

Clause 11.2   provides for Client Representative and Core Group review of any proposed Volume Supply Agreement.

Clause 11.3   provides for a Specialist Contract to be concluded adopting the prices and terms of any approved Volume Supply Agreement.

CLAUSE 12   PRICES *(See also Appendix 10 Flowchart E)*

Introduction   The initial Price Framework is agreed as a Partnering Document at the point of signing the Project Partnering Agreement *(see also Chapter 5.4)*. It should include:-

- the Client's Budget (if known);

- the Constructor's agreed Profit, Central Office Overheads and (if known) Site Overheads;

- known costs such as the prices agreed in respect of elements of the Project already fully designed and costed (if any);

- the amounts allowed in respect of risks to the Project already fully analysed (if any) and a statement as to the proposed costing of risks, including any amounts identified by the Constructor as prospective risk contingencies requiring review, analysis and management in accordance with the Partnering Contract.

It is important to identify in the initial Price Framework those amounts that are agreed as fixed sums; those amounts that are agreed as percentages (with provision as to when they may be converted into fixed sums); those amounts that are agreed provisionally with a statement of the procedure by which they will be firmed up; and those amounts that represent the perception of one Partnering Team member with a statement of the agreed analysis, review or other processes required before such amounts are agreed by other Partnering Team members.

As to the development of the Price Framework, in order to establish an Agreed Maximum Price with sufficient accuracy prior to commencement of the Project on Site, this clause provides for build-up of the prices of approved Direct Labour Packages, approved Preferred Specialists and selected tendered Specialists, the agreement of any discounts and other benefits, and the review of risks in accordance with clause 18.1 prior to the acceptance of any proposed risk contingency. The Agreed Maximum Price should be stated in the Commencement Agreement, and the developed Price Framework should be identified in the Commencement Agreement and signed as a Partnering Document at the time of entering into the Commencement Agreement.

Clause 12.1 provides for the Client to pay amounts stated in the Price Framework for performance of Constructor's Services, namely design or other services other than Pre-Possession Activities agreed to be performed by the Constructor prior to the date of the Commencement Agreement.

Clause 12.2 provides for the Client to pay amounts stated in any Pre-Possession Agreement for performance of agreed Pre-Possession Activities as further described in clauses 13.3 and 13.4 *(see also Chapter 4.5)*.

Clause 12.3 provides for development and agreement of an Agreed Maximum Price within any stated Budget and otherwise as low as achievable consistent with best value and in compliance with the Partnering Documents.

Clause 12.4 provides that agreed fixed amounts in the Price Framework for the Constructor's Profit, Central Office Overheads and Site Overheads, subject only to agreed variations, shall form part of the Agreed Maximum Price.

Clause 12.5 provides for the prices of Direct Labour Packages and Preferred Specialists to be included in relevant Business Cases submitted pursuant to clause 10.3.

Clause 12.6 provides that prices set out in each approved Business Case shall form part of the Agreed Maximum Price.

Clause 12.7 provides that prices deriving from Specialist tenders, submitted pursuant to clause 10.6, shall form part of the Agreed Maximum Price.

Clause 12.8 prohibits Specialist discounts or other benefits in favour of the Constructor unless expressly agreed.

Clause 12.9 restricts risk pricing, and provides that any proposed risk contingency shall be notified to the Client but shall not form part of the Agreed Maximum Price, except if and to the extent that it has first been approved by the Client after review of the relevant risk by the Constructor and other appropriate Partnering Team members with proposals for its elimination, reduction, insurance, sharing or apportionment and for removal or reduction of the relevant risk contingency *(see also clause 18 Risk Management)*.

Clause 12.10 provides for the Core Group to investigate the potential for cost savings and added value.

CLAUSE 13   INCENTIVES

Introduction This clause provides for agreed incentive arrangements, to be further detailed in the Partnering Documents, and encourages the Core Group to consider and seek additional incentive arrangements. The clause recognises typical techniques for incentivising additional effort on the part of Partnering Team members, such as the sharing of savings/added value that result from innovative proposals approved by the Client. It also identifies as incentives the structured approach to Pre-Possession Activities, and any agreed links between payment and the achievement of agreed KPI targets.

Clause 13.1   encourages the Core Group to consider and agree appropriate incentives *"to encourage Partnering Team members to maximise their efforts".*

Clause 13.2   provides for implementation of agreed shared savings arrangements and added value incentives, as described in the Project Partnering Agreement or otherwise recommended by the Core Group and approved by the Client.

Details of the agreed shared savings arrangements and/or added value incentives should be set out carefully in the Project Partnering Agreement with advice from the Partnering Adviser.

Clause 13.3   provides for payment in respect of Pre-Possession Activities, namely those activities other than Constructor's Services forming part of the Project and undertaken by the Constructor on or off Site prior to the Commencement Agreement.

Details of the agreed Pre-Possession Activities together with dates for their completion, arrangements for payment and other relevant terms should be set out in a Pre-Possession Agreement based on the form set out in PPC2000 Appendix 3 Part 1. It should be emphasised that a Pre-Possession Agreement cannot be signed in advance of the Project Partnering Agreement *(see also Chapter 4.5 and Appendix 3 Pre-Possession Agreement Checklist).*

Clause 13.4   deals with the contractual treatment of Pre-Possession Activities as regards Intellectual Property Rights, timing, payment, problem solving and avoidance or resolution of disputes. It also clarifies the limited effect of any Pre-Possession Agreement, the status of Pre-Possession Activities and their termination on request by the Client Representative.

Clause 13.5   provides for the agreement of any linkage between payment of the Constructor or any Consultant and achievement of the Date for Completion or any agreed KPI targets. This provides scope for the Partnering Team members to agree a wide range of performance-related incentives, which could relate to achievement of KPI targets for cost, time, defects, accidents or otherwise. It should be noted that there is no liquidated damages provision in PPC2000 and that any such provision, if required, would need to be incorporated in another Partnering Document pursuant to clause 13.5 or under clause 28 as a Special Term.

Clause 13.6   requires notification to and approval by the Client of any payment or benefit to a Partnering Team member not described in the Partnering Documents or in a Specialist Contract.

CLAUSE 14   PRE-CONDITIONS TO START ON SITE

Introduction   The central purpose of the early signing of the Project Partnering Agreement is to establish who does what and when during the pre-construction phase prior to unconditional start on Site. Review of the compliance by Partnering Team members with the pre-conditions set out in this clause, and any others set out in the Project Brief, is the test of whether or not these agreed activities have occurred and whether matters recognised by the Partnering Team members as outside their control have facilitated or obstructed the readiness of the Project to proceed on

Site. It is important that all Partnering Team members state clearly all known pre-conditions to start on Site: the clause recognises a list of pre-conditions, including for example Site acquisition and funding, and provides for any other pre-conditions to be set out in the Project Brief.

Clause 14.1   requires implementation *("completely or to such lesser extent as is stated in the Partnering Documents or is otherwise agreed by all Partnering Team members")* of pre-conditions to start on Site that include:

- agreement of the Project Timetable, development of the Health and Safety Plan, finalisation of Site surveys and investigations, and obtaining of relevant planning and other regulatory approvals;

- development of an integrated design, supply and construction process;

- selection and full involvement of Specialists;

- finalisation of an Agreed Maximum Price supported by a Price Framework;

- evidence of agreed insurances;

- finalisation of and satisfactory progress against agreed KPIs;

- completion of any required Site acquisition or Project funding and any other pre-conditions set out in the Project Brief.

Clause 14.2   requires Partnering Team members to use reasonable skill and care appropriate to their agreed roles, expertise and responsibilities to achieve satisfaction of the agreed pre-conditions and to notify each other when this has been achieved.

CLAUSE 15   PROJECT ON SITE

Introduction   This clause deals with signature of a Commencement Agreement based on the form set out in PPC2000 Appendix 3 Part 2 that triggers unconditional commencement of the Project on Site, and goes on to describe the practical rights and obligations of the Partnering Team members during the construction phase of the Project *(see also Chapter 4.6 and Appendix 4 Commencement Agreement Checklist)*.

Limited work on Site may have been previously authorised by a Pre-Possession Agreement, entered into after the Project Partnering Agreement but in advance of the Commencement Agreement.

Clause 15.1   provides for execution of the Commencement Agreement by all Partnering Team members as soon as the pre-conditions described in clause 14.1 have been satisfied, subject to prior circulation of the completed Commencement Agreement and allowing ten (10) Working Days for Partnering Team members' comments.

Clause 15.2   provides for the Constructor, with Partnering Team members' input as agreed, to carry out and complete the Project by the agreed Date for Completion (subject to extension in accordance with the Partnering Terms) and in consideration of the Client paying to the Constructor the Agreed Maximum Price (subject to agreed increases and decreases in accordance with the Partnering Terms).

Clause 15.3   establishes a licence for the Constructor to proceed with the Project on Site subject to agreed constraints on possession and access and other Partnering Team members' rights of access. It also states the Constructor's responsibility for Site security, and for the risk of loss and damage to the Project and relevant materials, goods and equipment on or off Site, and the Constructor's liability and indemnity in respect of injury, death, loss or damage affecting any person or property (other than property required to be insured under clause 19.1).

Clause 15.4   provides for ownership in materials, goods and equipment to pass to the Client when incorporated in the Project or when the Constructor receives payment (whichever shall be the earlier). It also provides for them not to be removed from Site and for their protection, storage, marking and insurance pending delivery to Site.

CLAUSE 16   QUALITY AND ENVIRONMENT

Introduction   This clause focuses on agreed quality issues and standards, and provides that a *"Quality Management System"* will be set out in the Partnering Documents. It is intended that the Partnering Team members should identify provisions for inspections, testing, sampling and other quality management techniques in specific sections of the Project Brief, Project Proposals and Consultant Services Schedules, so that they form a cohesive system that all Partnering Team members can understand and implement. The clause also deals with environmental risk, although specific obligations of Partnering Team members to eliminate or render negligible environmental risk should be stated in the Partnering Documents.

Clause 16.1   requires the Partnering Team to achieve agreed levels of quality as described in the Partnering Documents, and to seek in accordance with agreed KPIs to reduce defects, increase Project lifespan, improve Sustainability and reduce the cost of Project *"Operation"*.

Clause 16.2   requires the Partnering Team members to implement the Project to standards compliant with the Partnering Documents and otherwise appropriate to the Project.

Clause 16.3   provides for implementation of a Quality Management System as set out in the Project Brief, Project Proposals and Consultant Services Schedules.

Clause 16.4   requires Partnering Team members to implement agreed measures (to be stated in the Partnering Documents) to eliminate or render negligible the risk of *"Hazardous Substances"*, and to comply with *"Environmental Laws"*.

CLAUSE 17   CHANGE *(See also Appendix 10 Flowchart F)*

Introduction   This clause recognises the right of any Partnering Team member to propose a *"Change"*, in order to encourage Value Engineering and innovation throughout the life of the Project. The remainder of the clause deals with the system for advance evaluation of the time and cost consequences of a Change, which is the required approach unless the Client instructs that a Change should proceed without advance time/cost evaluation for reasons of urgency.

Clause 17.1   entitles any Partnering Team member to propose a Change to the Client, for its consideration with the Client Representative (and if appropriate under clause 23.4 the Core Group) advised by other Partnering Team members.

Clause 17.2   provides that any Change may be proposed by the Client (including an approved proposal under clause 17.1) by notification to the Constructor, and that (subject to its rights of objection under clauses 5.4 and 8.11) the Constructor shall submit within agreed time limits a *"Constructor's Change Submission"* comprising its proposals as to cost and time consequences.

Clause 17.3   deals with submission of a Constructor's Change Submission and the Client Representative's resultant instruction to proceed with the Change (with or without modification) or withdrawal of the proposed Change.

Clause 17.4   provides for evaluation of a Change by the Client Representative where the time and cost consequences are not agreed within 20 Working Days from its instruction, in the absence of or pending any notification and resolution of a disputed matter.

Clause 17.5   entitles the Client Representative to instruct implementation of an urgent Change in advance of a Constructor's Change Submission.

Clause 17.6   requires that any Constructor's Change Submission should minimise adverse effects on the Agreed Maximum Price and Date for Completion and that Partnering Team members should assist in achieving this.

Clause 17.7   provides for the binding effect of any Change, when finalised in accordance with clause 17, on the Partnering Team members.

Clause 17.8   recognises the potential for an equivalent adjustment in the time for performance of affected Consultant Services and for amendment of Consultant payment entitlements if so provided in their Consultant Payment Terms.

CLAUSE 18   RISK MANAGEMENT *(See also Appendix 10 Flowchart G)*

Introduction   PPC2000 offers new opportunities and techniques for collaborative risk management by creating the Partnering Team at the earliest opportunity and setting out the ways that they agree to tackle risk issues.

The Constructor's proposed costing of risks should be stated in the Price Framework at the time of signing the Project Partnering Agreement, including any amounts identified by the Constructor as prospective risk contingencies. The exercises by which the Partnering Team members will analyse and manage risk should be set out elsewhere in the Partnering Documents (e.g. Project Brief, Project Proposals and Consultant Services Schedules) so that the Client Representative can organise and monitor these in accordance with clause 5.1(iii).

Having fixed the Consultant's fees and pre-agreed the Constructor's Profit, where possible with shared incentives for cost reduction and added value, the Consultants and the Constructor (and any Specialists engaged on an equivalent basis) should have the same incentive as the Client to reduce the costs associated with a risk if the underlying risk itself can be reduced. Accordingly, throughout the period from signature of the Project Partnering Agreement, and in particular during the pre-construction phase prior to signature of the Commencement Agreement, there should be created an agreed system and a shared motivation for all Partnering Team members to analyse and manage identified risks and to minimise their costs.

The clause recognises the potential for risk sharing arrangements, and provides for these to be set out in the Commencement Agreement, if and to the extent that they are agreed to be the appropriate solution after Partnering Team members have completed risk analysis and management activities during the pre-construction phase. Subject to such risk sharing arrangements, the clause provides that the Constructor will be responsible for managing risks associated with the Project on Site, with the exception of agreed grounds for extension of time and costs arising from consequent delay or disruption.

The clause requires immediate Constructor notice (with evidence and proposals) in respect of any event of delay or disruption, with tight timescales for finalising their assessment. It sets out a clear basis for establishing the Constructor's entitlement to additional Site Overheads and reimbursement for unavoidable work or expenditure, with no other Constructor financial entitlements deriving from any event of delay or disruption. The clause also establishes the presumption that the Constructor will be responsible for the Site and its *"Environment"*, subject to agreed exceptions stated in the Commencement Agreement.

Clause 18.1 highlights the requirement for all Partnering Team members to undertake early Risk Management, in recognition of the risks involved in the design, supply and construction of the Project and the costs associated with those risks. Partnering Team members are *"to analyse and manage risks in the most effective ways including:*

> *(i) identifying risks and their likely costs;*
>
> *(ii) eliminating or reducing risks and their costs;*
>
> *(iii) insuring risks wherever affordable and appropriate;*
>
> *(iv) sharing or apportioning risks according to which one or more Partnering Team members are most able to manage such risks".*

Risk Management is the fourth key process that needs particular attention from the Partnering Team during the pre-construction phase (alongside design and process development under clause 8, supply chain development under clause 10 and price finalisation under clause 12). The analysis and management of risks relevant to the Project should be by a methodology agreed by the Partnering Team prior to signing the Project Partnering Agreement and reflected in activities described in the Partnering Documents, for example the preparation and agreement of a risk register with an agreed action plan as to how Partnering Team members will deal with the risks identified and any prospective risk contingencies *(see also clause 12.9)*. Such activities need to be linked to specific dates or periods in the Partnering Timetable and the Project Timetable.

Clause 18.2 provides for the Constructor to assume primary risk management responsibility from the date of the Commencement Agreement until Project Completion, except as otherwise stated in the Partnering Terms and in any agreed risk sharing arrangements (to be set out in the Commencement Agreement).

Clause 18.3 provides a list of grounds for extension of time, where despite the Constructor's best endeavours any listed matter adversely affects the Date for Completion. It is important to note that a claim for extension of time caused by a default or failure of the Client or any Consultant beyond an agreed time limit will be subject to the Constructor giving Early Warning to the Client not less than five (5) Working Days before expiry of such time limit (clause 18.3(i)), even though the time limit itself will be stated in the Partnering Terms or in the Project Timetable. Early Warning is also a pre-condition to the Constructor claiming an extension of time based on breach of the Partnering Contract by the Client or any Consultant (clause 18.3(xiv)).

There should be set out in the Commencement Agreement any adjustments to the agreed grounds for extension of time by way of third party consents (clause 18.3(iii)) and any additional events (clause 18.3(xvi)) entitling a claim for extension of time.

Clause 18.4   sets out the procedure for the Constructor to submit an extension of time application with appropriate evidence and proposals for minimising its effects, as soon as it is aware of an event under clause 18.3, for implementation of the Constructor's proposals and for the Client Representative to respond to the submission, all within strict time limits. It deals with the requirement for the Client Representative to evaluate a claim on a fair and reasonable basis and for the Client Representative's evaluation to prevail in the absence of or pending notification and resolution of any disputed matter.

Clause 18.5   entitles the Constructor to appropriate proportionate additional Site Overheads during a delay created by grounds entitling an extension of time (with listed exceptions). Any adjustments to the list of exceptions should be set out in the Commencement Agreement.

Clause 18.6   entitles the Constructor to claim for unavoidable work or expenditure properly required and resulting from the grounds entitling extension of time (with listed exceptions), whether or not they give rise to an extension of time. Any adjustment to the list of exceptions should be set out in the Commencement Agreement. This entitlement is subject to the Constructor minimising the amount of such additional work or expenditure, is subject to the exclusion of loss of profit claims, and additional Profit and Central Office Overheads, and is subject to the appropriate additional payment being the full extent of the Constructor's entitlement.

Clause 18.7   recognises the effect of extensions of time under clause 18 on the time for performance of affected Consultant Services, and for amendment of Consultant payment entitlements if so provided in their Consultant Payment Terms, in either case arising where the Consultant itself did not cause the relevant delay/ disruption.

Clause 18.8   establishes the Constructor's deemed satisfaction as to the extent of the Site, its boundaries and the nature of its surrounding Environment.

Clause 18.9   establishes the Constructor's responsibility, save as to "Antiquities" and any other agreed exceptions, to satisfy itself as to the state and condition of soil and rock strata and any structures and Environment comprising the Site. Any exceptions to the Constructor's acceptance of risk in respect of the Site should be stated in the Commencement Agreement, if and to the extent that such exceptions are agreed to be the appropriate solution after Partnering Team members have completed risk analysis and management activities during the pre-construction phase.

Clause 18.10   states the Constructor's responsibility in respect of delay or disruption caused by any Specialist (other than Specialists appointed direct by the Client under clause 10.11).

CLAUSE 19   INSURANCE AND SECURITY

Introduction   This clause should be read in conjunction with PPC2000 Appendix 4 and deals with the full range of customary insurances, including cover for the Project and the Site, third party liability insurance, professional indemnity insurance and product liability insurance. It also recognises the possibility of *"Environmental*

GUIDE to PPC2000 & SPC2000   © ACA and Trowers & Hamlins 2003

Risk Insurance" and *"Latent Defects Insurance"* and the desirability of *"Whole Project Insurance".* The last of these would be a pre-requisite to using the option amending the Partnering Team members' duty of care to a fixed proportion of loss or damage irrespective of contribution to its cause *(see also clause 22.1)*, as such an amended duty of care would not normally be supported by professional indemnity insurance. The clause deals in addition with any agreed security for payment or for the Constructor's performance.

Clause 19.1   provides for the insurance of the Project and the Site by a party named in the Commencement Agreement, in joint names and with waivers of subrogation as stated in the Commencement Agreement, for the risks stated in PPC2000 Appendix 4 Part 1 Section 1 and any additional or adjusted risks stated in the Commencement Agreement. It also provides for cover, if so stated, for third party property damage in the amount stated in the Commencement Agreement and for the risks stated in PPC2000 Appendix 4 Part 1 Section 2.

Clause 19.2   deals with procedures for repair and restoration of the Project in the event of a claim under the clause 19.1 insurance.

Clause 19.3   provides for third party liability insurance to be taken out by each Partnering Team member, for the amounts stated in the Project Partnering Agreement or any Joining Agreement, and for the risks stated in PPC2000 Appendix 4 Part 2.

Clause 19.4   provides for professional indemnity insurance or product liability insurance to be taken out by those Partnering Team members and for those amounts stated in the Project Partnering Agreement or any Joining Agreement, and for the risks stated in PPC2000 Appendix 4 Part 3.

Clause 19.5   provides for Environmental Risk Insurance if so stated in the Commencement Agreement.

Clause 19.6   provides for Latent Defects Insurance if so stated in the Commencement Agreement.

Clause 19.7   provides for Whole Project Insurance if so stated in the Commencement Agreement.

Clause 19.8   cross-refers to general insurance obligations set out in PPC2000 Appendix 4 Part 4.

Clause 19.9   deals with provision of any agreed advance payment guarantee, performance bond, parent company guarantee or retention bond if so stated in the Project Brief. Advice as for the forms of any such documents should be obtained from the Partnering Adviser.

CLAUSE 20   PAYMENT

Introduction   This clause encourages innovative payment systems, such as payment milestones, activity schedules or cashflows to be set out in the Price Framework, the Consultant Payment Terms and any Pre-Possession Agreement. In the absence of such provisions, it provides for payment in response to monthly applications by the Constructor and the Consultants.

Clause 20.1   establishes the payment obligations of the Client to the Consultants and the Constructor.

Clause 20.2	provides for the use of agreed payment milestones, activity schedules, cashflows or payment intervals, if set out in the Price Framework, the Consultant Payment Terms and any Pre-Possession Agreement, and otherwise provides for monthly payments to the Consultants and the Constructor, subject to applications with appropriate supporting details.
Clause 20.3	provides for payments to the Constructor by reference to valuations issued by the Client Representative, within stated periods unless otherwise agreed.
Clause 20.4	provides for payments to Consultants by reference to notices issued by the Client, within stated periods unless otherwise agreed.
Clause 20.5	describes the required content of Constructor valuations.
Clause 20.6	provides for final notification of any proposed withholding or deduction.
Clause 20.7	allows for adjustment of any valuation or notice in any subsequent valuation or notice.
Clause 20.8	provides that no valuation or notice constitutes approval of any works or services.
Clause 20.9	provides for interest on late payment at the rate stated in the Project Partnering Agreement.
Clause 20.10	provides for fluctuations only as set out in the Price Framework and Consultant Payment Terms.
Clause 20.11	provides for Constructor payment of Specialists in accordance with agreed Specialist Payment Terms, and for maintenance of full payment records.
Clause 20.12	allows for inspection by the Client Representative of the financial records of any other Partnering Team member.
Clause 20.13	provides for statutory deductions from Constructor payments.
Clause 20.14	provides for payment on Project Completion, within a stated period unless otherwise agreed. The clause includes the only reference in PPC2000 to *"Retention"*, deductible only if so stated in the Price Framework. Any proposed Retention should be considered in the light of alternative incentives for rectification of defects, and also by reference to the corresponding retention arrangements agreed between the Constructor and its Specialists and their practical implications and underlying cost.
Clause 20.15	provides for preparation and agreement of a *"Final Account"*, within a stated period unless otherwise agreed.
Clause 20.16	deals with non-agreement of the Final Account and consequent reference to agreed problem-solving and dispute avoidance or resolution procedures.
Clause 20.17	provides for Constructor and Consultant rights of suspension of performance in the event of non-payment.

GUIDE to PPC2000 & SPC2000   © ACA and Trowers & Hamlins 2003

CLAUSE 21   **PROJECT COMPLETION AND SUPPORT**

Introduction   This clause deals with handover of the completed Project. Particular arrangements for attendance, inspection and testing on Project Completion should be set out in the Project Brief, as should any time constraints on these procedures and any required pre-conditions. The clause also provides for a Defects Liability Period, and for the Core Group to consider proposals put forward by any Partnering Team member for Operation of the completed Project. The latter is intended to encourage all Partnering Team members to consider the potential for an ongoing role in the Project.

Clause 21.1   sets out the procedure for Project Completion by reference to an agreed notice period and subject to any exclusions and pre-conditions set out in the Project Brief.

Clause 21.2   provides for attendance, inspection and testing by the Client Representative and other appropriate Partnering Team members, with a procedure for either confirmation of Project Completion or the issue of a statement as to any non-compliance with Partnering Documents.

Clause 21.3   provides for part Project Completion by agreement.

Clause 21.4   sets out the Constructor's obligations for rectification of defects within an agreed Defects Liability Period stated in the Project Partnering Agreement.

Clause 21.5   provides for confirmation of rectification of defects by the Client Representative.

Clause 21.6   entitles the Constructor or any Consultant or Specialist Partnering Team member to submit proposals for Operation of the completed Project, and requires Core Group consideration of those proposals.

CLAUSE 22   **DUTY OF CARE AND WARRANTIES**

Introduction   This clause should be read in conjunction with the relevant options set out in the Project Partnering Agreement. Where parties outside the Partnering Team may need to offer or be offered collateral warranties, the Partnering Team members should consider the alternative of bringing such parties into the Partnering Contract itself or creating rights in accordance with the Contracts (Rights of Third Parties) Act 1999.

Clause 22.1   establishes the mutual duty of Partnering Team members to *"use reasonable skill and care appropriate to their respective roles, expertise and responsibilities as stated in the Partnering Documents"*.

This duty of care may be amended by agreement, whether under the options set out in the Project Partnering Agreement or otherwise. Any amendment to the agreed duty of care must be drafted very carefully and reconciled with the other provisions of the Partnering Contract and the duty of care of other Partnering Team members. The options set out in the Project Partnering Agreement are as follows:-·

● For the Constructor to accept full responsibility for all aspects of the Project irrespective of the contributions of any other Partnering Team member, but without prejudice to the duty of care of other Partnering Team members to the Constructor. This is intended to establish single point responsibility of the Constructor for the Project;·

- For the Constructor to warrant that the *"completed Project shall be fit for its intended purposes as described in the Project Brief"*. It should be noted that this warranty may be in conflict with the Constructor's professional indemnity insurance and should only be offered and accepted if it is supported by such insurance;

- For the responsibility of any named Partnering Team member to be limited to a proportion of any loss or damage that is *"just and equitable"* having regard to the extent of its responsibility and on the basis that each other Partnering Team member shall also be deemed to have paid its just and equitable proportion (often referred to as a *"net contribution"* clause);

- For responsibility of Partnering Team members to be limited to fixed proportions of any loss or damage irrespective of the extent of their respective contributions to its cause. It should be noted that this option is likely to be in conflict with Partnering Team members' professional indemnity insurance, and should only be considered if it can be supported by an agreed policy of Whole Project Insurance that operates in substitution for such professional indemnity insurance *(see also clause 19.7)*.

Any other amendment to the duty of care of any Partnering Team member should be stated in the Project Partnering Agreement.

In all matters relating to the duty of care of Partnering Team members, advice should be obtained from the Partnering Adviser and notification should be made to Partnering Team members' professional indemnity insurers.

Clause 22.2   provides for any required collateral warranties to be stated in the Project Partnering Agreement and in forms to be annexed to the Project Partnering Agreement. Advice as to the forms of any such collateral warranties should be obtained from the Partnering Adviser.

Clause 22.3   provides for direct Specialist warranties in favour of the Client where so described in the Project Brief or Project Proposals or otherwise available.

Clause 22.4   excludes the operation of the Contracts (Rights of Third Parties) Act 1999 except as otherwise stated in the Project Partnering Agreement.

CLAUSE 23   KEY PERFORMANCE INDICATORS AND CONTINUOUS IMPROVEMENT

Introduction   This clause provides for the assessment of performance of all Partnering Team members by the Core Group using the agreed KPIs. Accordingly, any rewards or remedies that are triggered by performance against agreed KPI targets will be effective only if the Core Group reach Consensus in their assessment of the relevant Partnering Team member's performance. The clause deals with the Open-book monitoring of progress against the agreed KPIs and states that the Core

GUIDE to PPC2000 & SPC2000   © ACA and Trowers & Hamlins 2003

Group should investigate proposals submitted by any Partnering Team member for achieving continuous improvement by reference to the criteria set out in the KPIs. The clause also deals with the requirement for a post-Project Completion review.

Clause 23.1   provides for performance of each Partnering Team member to be kept under regular review by the Core Group by reference to agreed KPIs.

Clause 23.2   requires Partnering Team members to provide information on an Open-book basis to demonstrate progress against the agreed KPIs.

Clause 23.3   provides for Partnering Team members to maximise through measurable continuous improvement the potential of the Project to achieve the agreed objectives and to provide best value to the Client, and for them to refine and improve processes for the benefit of the Project and future projects.

Clause 23.4   provides for Core Group review of proposals for continuous improvement.

Clause 23.5   links criteria for continuous improvement to the KPIs, subject to revisions recommended by the Core Group and agreed by Partnering Team members.

Clause 23.6   provides for a Partnering Team meeting after Project Completion for performance review and for consideration of the scope for further improvement on future projects.

CLAUSE 24   JOINT INITIATIVES AND STRATEGIC ALLIANCING

Introduction   PPC2000 is a Project Partnering Contract and in its published form is appropriate only for use in respect of a single Project. However, PPC2000 is often used for procurement of each of a number of Projects within a strategic alliancing arrangement. Partnering Team members are encouraged by this clause firstly to explore joint initiatives for the benefit of the Project and secondly to develop strategic alliancing arrangements for the implementation of further projects, subject to performance and agreement of specific terms.

Clause 24.1   recognises the potential for joint initiatives for the benefit of the Project as agreed between Partnering Team members after Core Group consideration.

Clause 24.2   recognises the potential for strategic alliancing on further projects subject to performance against agreed KPI targets and subject to agreement of specific terms consistent with current applicable laws and regulations.

CLAUSE 25   GENERAL

Introduction   This general clause deals with exclusion of partnership, amendment to the Partnering Contract, applicable laws and regulations, and confidentiality.

Clause 25.1   excludes any partnership between Partnering Team members.

Clause 25.2   prohibits assignment or sub-contracting except as agreed or in accordance with the Partnering Terms. Any agreed rights of assignment should be stated in the Project Partnering Agreement.

Clause 25.3 states that the Partnering Documents are comprehensive and provides that no amendment to the Partnering Contract shall be binding unless signed by all Partnering Team members or otherwise made in accordance with the Partnering Terms.

Clause 25.4 requires compliance by Partnering Team members with all current laws and regulations in force in the country stated in the Project Partnering Agreement and in the country where the Site is located.

Clause 25.5 restricts disclosure of confidential information.

CLAUSE 26   TERMINATION

Introduction This clause states firstly the right of the Client to terminate the appointment of all Partnering Team members prior to the date of the Commencement Agreement, in the event of any failure to satisfy agreed pre-conditions or for any other reason not reasonably foreseeable by the Client. This right is necessary to retain reasonable flexibility for the Client in line with creation of the Partnering Contract and the Partnering Team as early as possible in the pre-construction phase of the Project, namely prior to agreement of the designs, risk treatment, supply chain arrangements and prices necessary to satisfy the Client that the Project will meet its requirements. The remainder of the clause deals with other grounds for termination, such as insolvency or breach by a Partnering Team member, and also the possibility of suspension or abandonment of the Project by reason of specified risks beyond the control of any Partnering Team member.

Clause 26.1 provides for Client termination of all Partnering Team members' appointments in the event of failure to satisfy agreed pre-conditions under clause 14.1 or if for any other reason not reasonably foreseeable by the Client it no longer wishes to proceed with the Project. Such termination may occur only prior to the Commencement Agreement and entitles Partnering Team members to payment of all amounts due in respect of expressly approved activities carried out prior to termination but no other amounts.

Clause 26.2 provides for automatic termination of any Partnering Team member's appointment upon its bankruptcy or insolvency, and for automatic termination of all other Partnering Team members' appointments upon the Client's bankruptcy or insolvency.

Clause 26.3 provides for termination of the appointment of any Consultant or Specialist Partnering Team member for any material breach, subject to prior Core Group review.

Clause 26.4 provides for termination of the Constructor's appointment for listed breaches, subject to prior Core Group review, and for completion of the Project using others.

Clause 26.5 provides for any Partnering Team member to terminate its appointment for listed Client breaches, subject to prior Core Group review, and for payment of amounts properly due to that Partnering Team member.

Clause 26.6 provides for suspension or abandonment of the Project if it is impossible to proceed for stated reasons outside the Partnering Team members' control and despite their best endeavours.

GUIDE to PPC2000 & SPC2000   © ACA and Trowers & Hamlins 2003

Clause 26.7   provides for automatic abandonment after three months' suspension (unless otherwise agreed by all Partnering Team members) and for the consequent termination of all Partnering Team members' appointments and payment of amounts properly due.

Clause 26.8   requires the Constructor to protect and secure the Project in the event of termination of its appointment or suspension or abandonment of the Project.

Clause 26.9   provides for replacement of any Consultant in the event of termination of its appointment, subject to Constructor approval after Core Group Consultation.

Clause 26.10   provides for notice of proposed termination of its appointment by any Client-appointed Specialist that is a Partnering Team member.

Clause 26.11   provides for notice of proposed termination of its appointment by any Constructor-appointed Specialist that is a Partnering Team member.

Clause 26.12   provides that termination of its appointment for Client breach, by any Client-appointed Specialist that is a Partnering Team member, will be a Client breach of the Partnering Contract.

Clause 26.13   provides that termination of its appointment for Constructor breach, by any other Specialist that is a Partnering Team member, will be a Constructor breach of the Partnering Contract.

Clause 26.14   provides for the ongoing effect of the Partnering Contract notwithstanding termination of any Partnering Team member's appointment.

Clause 26.15   preserves the accrued mutual rights and obligations of Partnering Team members irrespective of termination.

CLAUSE 27   PROBLEM SOLVING AND DISPUTE AVOIDANCE OR RESULUTION

Introduction   PPC2000 recognises the importance of avoiding adjudication, arbitration or litigation of any difference or dispute in order to ensure that, despite any problems between them, the Partnering Team members can maintain the Open-book systems and integrated relationships and processes necessary to achieve their objectives. This clause sets out a number of alternative means of resolving a difference or dispute, commencing with immediate notification and reference to an agreed Problem-Solving Hierarchy, and providing for reference secondly to the Core Group and thirdly to conciliation, mediation or other agreed means of alternative dispute resolution. None of these procedures affect the statutory right of any Partnering Team member to refer a difference or dispute to adjudication at any time. The clause also provides for litigation or arbitration as agreed, for the agreed governing law and jurisdiction of the Partnering Contract and for an agreed limitation period for any claims and proceedings.

Clause 27.1   requires immediate notification of any difference or dispute between Partnering Team members, copied to the Client Representative.

Clause 27.2   provides for an agreed Problem-Solving Hierarchy. This should be set out in or annexed to the Commencement Agreement and advice on its format should be obtained from the Partnering Adviser.

Clause 27.3   provides for Core Group review of any difference or dispute that is not resolved through the Problem-Solving Hierarchy.

Clause 27.4   provides for conciliation (in accordance to the ACA Conciliation Procedure and PPC2000 Appendix 5 Part 1) or mediation or any other form of dispute resolution recommended by the Partnering Adviser, to be implemented in the event that the difference or dispute is not resolved through Core Group review.

Clause 27.5   provides for adjudication of any difference or dispute (in accordance with the Construction Industry Council Model Adjudication Procedure and PPC2000 Appendix 5 Part 2), irrespective of the procedures set out under clauses 27.1, 27.2, 27.3 and 27.4.

Clause 27.6   provides for litigation (or arbitration in accordance with the procedure set out in PPC2000 Appendix 5 Part 3, if so stated in the Project Partnering Agreement) of any difference or dispute not resolved by adjudication.

Clause 27.7   provides that the Partnering Contract shall be subject to the governing law and jurisdiction of the country stated in the Project Partnering Agreement.

Clause 27.8   provides for an agreed period of limitations to be stated in the Project Partnering Agreement, running from the Completion Date.

CLAUSE 28   SPECIAL TERMS

Clause 28 provides for any *"Special Terms"* agreed between Partnering Team members to be set out in or attached to the Project Partnering Agreement or the Commencement Agreement.

CHAPTER 7 - SPC2000

7.1 INTRODUCTION

SPC2000 is the ACA Standard Form of Specialist Contract for Project Partnering, launched by Sir Michael Latham in March 2002 after trialling by seven leading Constructors and after detailed review by organisations representing a range of Specialist sub-contractors. SPC2000 is wholly consistent with PPC2000. It should be entered into between the Constructor and its Specialist sub-contractors, including those Specialist sub-contractors who are also signatories to the PPC2000 Project Partnering Agreement or a Joining Agreement *(See also Chapter 2.6)*.

This chapter explains the range of Specialists for which SPC2000 is most suitable. It goes on to describe the structure of the SPC2000 *"Specialist Agreement"* and to comment on the SPC2000 *"Specialist Terms"* to the extent that they add to or amend the corresponding PPC2000 Partnering Terms. Additional words and expressions used in SPC2000 and in this chapter are defined in Appendix 1 to the SPC2000 Specialist Terms.

7.2 WHY A SEPARATE SPECIALIST CONTRACT?

PPC2000 is unique in the construction industry as a multi-party contract, establishing common terms of appointment for all Consultants and the Constructor, and also establishing the basis for integration of the role of Specialists in the processes of risk management, design development and partnering.

However, PPC2000 does not deal with sub-division of the performance and supply of services, works and goods for or to the Constructor by its range of Specialist sub-consultants, sub-contractors and suppliers, or with the sub-division of payments to be made by the Constructor to those Specialists. The terms of such performance, supply and payment vary considerably between the different types of Specialists and are broken down in different ways for different Projects. Accordingly, the diverse relationships between the Constructor and its Specialists need to be set out in separate forms of Specialist Contract.

7.3 SPECIALIST SUB-CONSULTANTS

SPC2000 can be used to govern relationships between the Constructor and its Specialist sub-consultants, although it should be noted that the majority of the typical terms of a sub-consultancy agreement are already expressed in PPC2000. Therefore, it is possible instead for the relationships between the Constructor and its Specialist sub-consultants to be incorporated into PPC2000 (without using SPC2000) by adding Special Terms under clause 28 of the PPC2000 Partnering Terms to state those terms dealing with the supply of and payment for sub-consultant services that are not already contained in the PPC2000 Partnering Terms. Alternatively, where a Specialist sub-consultant enters into a Joining Agreement, the PPC2000 Partnering Terms can be incorporated by reference, subject to the addition of such Special Terms as appropriate. Where Special Terms are added to PPC2000 or a Joining Agreement to cover the appointment of a Specialist sub-consultant, they need to be drafted carefully, and advice should be obtained from the Partnering Adviser.

7.4 SPECIALIST SUPPLIERS

As regards Specialist suppliers, the supply of their materials, goods and equipment is frequently governed by simple forms of Specialist Contract that may comprise or be based on the Specialist suppliers' own standard terms, or a Volume Supply Agreement *(See also clause 11 of the PPC2000 Partnering Terms)*, or the Constructor's own standard terms. In all cases, it is unlikely that SPC2000 will be appropriate for relationships between the Constructor and its Specialist suppliers unless the supply arrangements are complex or are combined with works undertaken by that Specialist supplier on or off Site.

7.5 SPECIALIST SUB-CONTRACTORS

Accordingly, the majority of cases where SPC2000 is likely to be used relate to relationships between the Constructor and its Specialist sub-contractors.

7.6 SPC2000 SPECIALIST AGREEMENT

The SPC2000 Specialist Agreement mirrors many of the provisions of the PPC2000 Project Partnering Agreement. It is a two-party document to be signed by the Constructor and the relevant Specialist, defining the *"Specialist Works"* as part of the Project. It assumes that a PPC2000 Project Partnering Agreement has already been entered into between the Client, the Constructor and others. The Specialist Agreement cross-refers to stated SPC2000 Specialist Terms:-

Clause 1.2   refers to the relevant PPC2000 Partnering Contract and records whether the Specialist is itself a party to the Partnering Contract or otherwise has been provided with a copy of all or part of it.

Clause 2   records the roles, expertise and responsibilities of the Constructor and the Specialist as described in the following *"Specialist Documents"*:-

- The SPC2000 Specialist Agreement and Specialist Terms;

- The *"Specialist Works Brief"*, which may comprise one or more documents listed in the Specialist Agreement;

- The *"Specialist Works Proposals"*, which may comprise one or more documents listed in the Specialist Agreement;

- The *"Specialist Timetable"*, which may be set out in a separate document or in a section of the Specialist Works Brief or may comprise only the key dates set out in the Specialist Agreement itself;

- The *"Specialist Payment Terms"*, which may be set out in a separate document or in a section of the Specialist Works Brief;

- Any *"Specialist KPIs"* which may be set out in a separate document or in a section of the Specialist Works Brief;

- The Partnering Contract or specified parts of the Partnering Contract.

Clauses 6, 8 and 15   set out whether or not the Constructor and the Specialist agree a separate Specialist Timetable, state key dates governing the Specialist Works, and provide for the following:-

- Specified stages, to be commenced within specified periods from service of *"Commencement Notices"* by the Constructor, which themselves are to be served by specified earliest and latest dates and become Specialist Documents;

- Periods for the Constructor to provide required designs and other information, for the Specialist to provide specified design submissions/ contributions and other information, for Constructor comments, for Specialist re-submission and for Value Engineering, all in relation to specified stages of design development;

- As appropriate, a period for procurement, fabrication and delivery to Site;

- As appropriate, a period for implementation on Site;

- An agreed *"Date for Specialist Completion"*, which may be expressed as a set date or as a period from a specified date or event;

- If appropriate, a statement of *"Specialist Sections"*;

- As appropriate, confirmation of exclusive or non-exclusive Constructor possession of the Site and relevant constraints, procedures and arrangements by reference to stated other Specialist Documents.

Clauses 8 and 11	state whether or not the Specialist is a member of the Design Team and record any amendment to the design development process set out in clause 8 of the Specialist Terms. They also state who is responsible for any required Site surveys and investigations, and list any Volume Supply Agreements to be utilised by the Specialist.
Clauses 12 and 13	state the Specialist Price and any agreed shared savings arrangements and added value incentives applicable to the Specialist.
Clauses 14 and 15	state any pre-conditions to issue of Commencement Notices for the Specialist Works, and set out the agreed dates or events when risk and/or ownership in specified materials, goods and equipment passes to the Constructor.
Clause 18	states any agreed risk sharing arrangements between the Constructor and the Specialist, any third party consents entitling a claim for extension of time, any additional events (beyond those stated in clause 18.3 of the Specialist Terms) entitling an extension of time, any adjusted extensions of time entitling a claim for additional Site Overheads or unavoidable work or expenditure, and any exceptions and clarifications in respect of Specialist risk as to the Site Environment.
Clause 19	sets out agreed arrangements in respect of insurance of the Project and Site, which should mirror those in the relevant PPC2000 Partnering Contract, and confirms the Specialist levels of third party liability, professional indemnity and product liability insurance as appropriate, together with the amount and form of any agreed Specialist advance payment guarantee, performance bond, parent company guarantee or retention bond.
Clause 20	describes payment arrangements under the Specialist Agreement comprising the date for commencement of the first interval until submission of a payment application, any revised periods for issue of valuations and for payments (if varied from of those stated in clause 20.3 of the Specialist Terms), the agreed rate of interest on late payment, any revised period for issue of an account following *"Specialist Completion"* (if varied from that stated in clause 20.12 of the Specialist Terms), and the agreed date or event triggering issue of the *"Specialist Final Account"*.

Clause 21   records the agreed *"Specialist Defects Liability Period"* and the agreed time limits for rectification of defects.

Clause 22   records any agreed amended duties of care, warranties and third party rights between the Constructor and the Specialist, any required collateral warranties and any agreed rights of assignment.

Clause 27   records the applicable law and courts with jurisdiction, which should correspond to those in the relevant PPC2000 Partnering Contract, and a *"Specialist Problem-Solving Hierarchy"*. It states the agreed conciliator and adjudicator, unless the procedures in SPC2000 Appendix 4 Part 1 and Appendix 4 Part 2 are agreed to govern their respective selection, and it states the agreed appointor of an arbitrator if arbitration is stated to be applicable. It also states the agreed period of limitations.

Clause 28   records any *"Specialist Special Terms"* that apply, set out in or attached to the Specialist Agreement by reference to clause 28 of the Specialist Terms.

In all respects it is envisaged that the Specialist Agreement will be consistent and integrated with the relevant PPC2000 Partnering Contract. One responsibility of the Partnering Adviser under clause 5.6 of the PPC2000 Partnering Terms will be to review Specialist Contracts for consistency with the Partnering Documents, whether individually or on a generic basis, in order to permit approval by the Client of each proposed form of Specialist Contract in accordance with clause 10.9 of the PPC2000 Partnering Terms.

The Constructor and the Specialist may sign the Specialist Agreement or execute it as a deed. Logically this should correspond to the manner in which the Partnering Team members have entered into the relevant PPC2000 Project Partnering Agreement.

When utilising SPC2000 and entering into Specialist Agreements incorporating appropriate Specialist Documents, the Constructor and the other Partnering Team members should have in mind the objective of fulfilling their obligations under clause 10.1 of the PPC2000 Partnering Terms *"to establish Specialist relationships in relation to all aspects of the Project that:-*

    (i)   *are Open-book to the maximum achievable extent;*

    (ii)   *clearly reflect the agreed requirements of the Client, the interests of the Partnering Team members and the needs of the Project;*

    (ii)   *secure the best available Specialist warranties and support and maximise the potential for Specialist innovation and other contributions to the Project;*

    (iii)   *establish and demonstrate best value to the Client;*

    (v)   *establish, wherever possible, partnering relationships complementary to those described in the Partnering Contract."*

7.7 SPECIALIST TERMS

The SPC2000 Specialist Terms substantially mirror the PPC2000 Partnering Terms and thereby enable the Constructor to pass down to each of its Specialists (whether or not they are members of the Partnering Team) agreed roles, responsibilities, rights and obligations consistent with those accepted by the Constructor with other Partnering Team members under the PPC2000 Partnering Contract.

Where no comment has been made in this chapter, it may be assumed that the Specialist Terms are substantially the same as the equivalent PPC2000 Partnering Terms on a clause by clause basis, subject to those PPC2000 Partnering Terms that are omitted because they are not relevant to the Constructor/ Specialist relationship.

Any new or amended provisions in the Specialist Terms, when compared to the PPC2000 Partnering Terms are described below, annotated with cross-references to the relevant clauses of the Specialist Terms:-

Clause 1	**Specialist Works and Project**

This clause identifies separately the Specialist Contract and PPC2000 Partnering Contract and defines the roles and responsibilities of the Constructor and the Specialist as being to *"work together and individually in the spirit of trust, fairness and mutual cooperation for the benefit of the Specialist Works and the Project, within the scope of their agreed roles, expertise and responsibilities as stated in the Specialist Documents"* (1.3).

Clause 2	**Specialist Documents**

This clause states that the Specialist Documents describe the roles, expertise and responsibilities of the Constructor and the Specialist, hence the importance of including the relevant PPC2000 Partnering Contract as a Specialist Document if appropriate (2.1). This clause also states that in the event of any discrepancy between the PPC2000 Partnering Contract and the Specialist Contract that cannot be resolved *"fairly and constructively without adversely affecting the agreed cost or time for completion or quality of the Specialist Works or the Project"*, and except where a different order of priority is agreed, the Specialist Contract shall prevail (2.4 and 2.6). It also requires the Constructor to notify the Specialist of any date or event under the PPC2000 Partnering Contract that is stated in the Specialist Contract to have an effect on the Specialist Contract (2.7).

Clause 3	**Communication and Organisation**

A separate Early Warning system operates between the Constructor and the Specialist, but there is no Core Group role under SPC2000 (3.3). Therefore notification and agreed action, for the purposes of an Early Warning given pursuant to the Specialist Contract, is a matter only between the Constructor and the Specialist.

Meetings between the Constructor and Specialist shall be as stated in the Specialist Timetable or when otherwise necessary to facilitate performance of their agreed roles and responsibilities, and may be called by either the Constructor or the Specialist in accordance with a stated procedure (3.4).

Clause 4	**Partnering Objectives**

These provisions relate to any agreed Specialist KPIs, as distinct from the PPC2000 Partnering Contract KPIs, although it is envisaged that the two sets of KPIs should be consistent.

Clause 5   **Constructor Instructions**

Unlike clause 5.3 of the PPC2000 Partnering Terms, pursuant to which the Client Representative *"may"* issue instructions to the Constructor where *"necessary and without prejudicing the collaborative spirit of the partnering relationships"*, clause 5.1 of the Specialist Terms provides that the Constructor *"shall issue such instructions to the Specialist as are necessary to enable the Specialist to implement the Specialist Works in accordance with the Specialist Documents"*.

Although the Specialist has a right of objection to Constructor instructions, clause 5.3 provides for the right of the Constructor to require immediate compliance with an instruction if justified by health and safety reasons or other demonstrable emergency, subject only to the Specialist's right to give Early Warning.

This clause also makes clear that the Specialist shall not comply with any instruction of a party other than the Constructor, and shall notify the Constructor immediately if any such instruction is issued (5.5). For the avoidance of doubt, it is stated that the Client Representative has no role, expertise or responsibilities under the Specialist Contract unless otherwise agreed (5.6). Any such agreement should be set out in Specialist Special Terms or in the Specialist Works Brief.

There is no stated role for the Partnering Adviser under SPC2000.

Clause 6   **Specialist Timetable**

This clause describes the status of a single Specialist Timetable governing the entire duration of the Constructor/Specialist relationship, and therefore likely to span aspects of both the Partnering Timetable and the Project Timetable under the relevant PPC2000 Partnering Contract. It is envisaged that the Specialist Timetable will be in place at the point of signing the SPC2000 Specialist Agreement, recording (whether in the Specialist Agreement or in a section of the Specialist Works Brief or in a separate Specialist Timetable) each key stage of the Specialist Works and any pre-conditions to implementation of each such stage.

Clause 7   **Health and Safety, Site Welfare and Employees**

Unlike clause 7 of the PPC2000 Partnering Terms, under which exclusion of individuals from the Project and Site is subject to prior Core Group Consultation, the Constructor has a right without such Consultation to require exclusion from the Specialist Works, the Project and the Site of any individual employed by the Specialist, or for whom it is responsible, who disrupts or otherwise adversely affects the Specialist Works or the Project.

Clause 8   **Design and Process Development**

This clause governs the respective design responsibilities of the Constructor and the Specialist as stated in the Specialist Documents. These should be fully integrated with design and process development under the relevant PPC2000 Partnering Contract. Any agreed amendment to the Specialist design development process set out in clause 8 should be clearly described in the Specialist Agreement and also in the Specialist Works Brief and the Specialist Works Proposals.

GUIDE to PPC2000 & SPC2000   © ACA and Trowers & Hamlins 2003

Clause 9   **Intellectual Property**

This clause mirrors the mutual warranty and indemnity in clause 9 of the PPC2000 Partnering Terms in respect of Intellectual Property Rights. The licence in clause 9.2 to copy and use designs and documents extends to completion and Operation of the Specialist Works and the remainder of the Project, in order to support the Constructor's licence under clause 9.2 of the PPC2000 Partnering Terms.

Clause 10   **Sub-Specialists**

SPC2000 recognises that a fully integrated supply chain will extend beyond the Specialist to its *"Sub-Specialist"* appointments, all of which are subject to prior Constructor approval (10.1). In dealing with Sub-Specialists, this clause states that the Specialist should apply principles equivalent to those that applied to its own appointment pursuant to clause 10.1 of the PPC2000 Partnering Terms, and should seek to establish relationships that wherever possible are complementary to the relationship described in the Specialist Contract and that incorporate relevant terms consistent with the Specialist Contract (10.1). The clause also confirms the Specialist's responsibility for Sub-Specialists (10.2), the requirement for Constructor Consultation prior to the termination of any Sub-Specialist appointment and for the Constructor's prior approval to the appointment of any replacement Sub-Specialist (10.3). Finally, it states that only the Specialist has authority to issue instructions to any Sub-Specialist (10.4).

Clause 11   **Volume Supply Agreements**

This clause requires utilisation of any Volume Supply Agreements stated in the Specialist Agreement.

Clause 12   **Specialist Price**

This clause provides for payment of agreed amounts stated in any *"Specialist Pre-Possession Agreement"* (12.1), and for the agreement of a *"Specialist Price"* as set out in the Specialist Payment Terms or otherwise established in accordance with the Specialist Terms, incorporating any stated agreed amounts for the Specialist's Profit, Central Office Overheads and Site Overheads (12.2, 12.3).

Where *"Specialist Budgets"* are stated in the Specialist Payment Terms, any relevant part of the Specialist Price will be established by the methods stated in the Specialist Payment Terms, within the periods stated in the Specialist Timetable (12.4).

Clause 13   **Incentives**

Shared savings arrangements and added value incentives applicable to the Specialist will be those stated in the Specialist Agreement (13.2). Provision is made for signature, if agreed, of a Specialist Pre-Possession Agreement based on the form set out in SPC2000 Appendix 2 Part 1 to authorise any agreed *"Specialist Pre-Possession Activities"* on or off Site prior to satisfaction of the pre-conditions described in clause 14 (13.3, 13.4). This allows the Constructor to utilise appropriate Specialists in fulfilling its own obligations under a relevant PPC2000 Pre-Possession Agreement. This clause also provides for agreement of any links between payment and achievement of the Date for Specialist Completion or any targets stated in the Specialist KPIs (13.5).

As in the case of PPC2000, the SPC2000 Specialist Contract does not provide for liquidated and ascertained damages, although these are one of the links between payment and achievement of Specialist KPIs that could be incorporated pursuant to clause 13.5.

Clause 14   **Pre-Conditions**

Implementation of the Specialist Works is subject to satisfaction of pre-conditions for commencement of the Project on Site stated in the PPC2000 Partnering Contract, and any further pre-conditions stated in the Specialist Agreement, either completely or to such lesser extent as the Constructor and the Specialist may agree.

Clause 15   **Implementation of Specialist Works**

SPC2000 provides for the issue of Commencement Notices based on the form set out in SPC2000 Appendix 2 Part 2 and in accordance with the Specialist Timetable, for commencement of relevant parts of the Specialist Works within agreed periods from the dates of any such Commencement Notices and for implementation and completion of the Specialist Works by the Date for Specialist Completion (subject to extension in accordance with the Specialist Terms). There is provision in the form of Commencement Notice for receipt to be acknowledged by the Specialist, although the trigger for commencement of the Specialist Works or any part is the issue of the Commencement Notice rather than acknowledgement of its receipt (15.1, 15.2).

The clause also requires the Specialist to use reasonable skill and care appropriate to its agreed role, expertise and responsibilities to integrate the Specialist Works with the remainder of the Project, and to integrate its activities with those of the Constructor and other Partnering Team members and *"Other Specialists"* (15.3(ii)).

The clause recognises the Constructor's responsibility for security of the Project and Site subject to any other arrangements stated in the Specialist Documents (15.3(iv)).

Risk in materials, goods and equipment intended for (or for use in connection with) the Specialist Works remains with the Specialist until Specialist Completion subject to other stated Specialist Terms and any exceptions stated in the Specialist Agreement (15.3(v)). Transfer of ownership of materials, goods and equipment intended for the Specialist Works occurs when they are incorporated in the Project or when the Specialist receives payment for them or on such other date or event as it is stated in the Specialist Agreement, whichever shall be the earlier (15.4).

In performance of its agreed role, expertise and responsibilities, the Specialist is required by this clause to provide the Constructor with information and assistance necessary to enable the Constructor to comply with its obligations under the relevant PPC2000 Partnering Contract, and not by reason of its own delay, default or failure to place the Constructor in breach of the PPC2000 Partnering Contract (15.5).

Clause 16   **Quality and Environment**

This clause provides for the Constructor and the Specialist to work to agreed quality and standards set out in the Specialist Documents and to implement an agreed *"Specialist Quality Management System"* to be set out in the Specialist Works Brief and the Specialist Works Proposals.

Clause 17   **Specialist Change**

This clause provides for a *"Specialist Change"* procedure which mirrors the Change procedure under clause 17 of the PPC2000 Partnering Terms, with adjusted timescales for integration with PPC2000. Accordingly, when the Constructor proposes a Specialist Change, the Specialist is required to submit a *"Specialist Change Submission"* within nine (9) Working Days and the Constructor is required to respond to that Specialist Change Submission within a further ten (10) Working Days instructing the Specialist to proceed (with or without modification) or withdrawing the Change (17.2, 17.3). If the time and cost effects of a Specialist Change are not agreed within fifteen (15) Working Days from the date of an instruction to proceed, then the Constructor shall ascertain such time and cost effects on a fair and reasonable basis, which will remain effective as the Specialist's entitlement in the absence of notification of a dispute within a further fifteen (15) Working Days or pending resolution of such a dispute (17.4).

Clause 18   **Risk Management**

Risk management obligations, scope for risk sharing arrangements and agreed grounds for extension of time mirror those in clause 18 of the PPC2000 Partnering Terms, with adjusted timescales for integration with PPC2000. Accordingly, the requirement for Early Warning in respect of delay caused by a default or failure of the Constructor is six (6) Working Days before expiry of the agreed time limit (18.3(i)), the period for the Constructor to issue an instruction overriding Specialist proposals for overcoming a delay event and minimising its adverse effects is four (4) Working Days (18.4(ii)), and the period for the Constructor's response to Specialist notification of a delay event and related unavoidable work or expenditure is twenty-five (25) Working Days (18.4). Such response governs the Specialist's time and cost entitlement in the absence of Specialist notification of a dispute within a further fifteen (15) Working Days or pending resolution of such dispute (18.4).

This clause also describes the Specialist's responsibility in respect of the state and condition of the Environment comprising the Site, insofar as it affects the Specialist Works (18.7), and states the Specialist's responsibility for any delay or disruption caused by Sub-Specialists (18.8).

Clause 19   **Insurance and Security**

This clause reflects equivalent insurance obligations to those set out in clause 19 of the PPC2000 Partnering Terms. As regards Environmental Risk Insurance, Latent Defects Insurance and Whole Project Insurance, it cross-refers to equivalent provisions in the relevant PPC2000 Partnering Contract (19.5, 19.6, 19.7).

Clause 20   **Payment**

This clause provides for payment in accordance with milestones, activity schedules or cashflows and any other payment arrangements set out in the Specialist Payment Terms, and provides for payment at monthly intervals if not otherwise agreed (20.2). Payments are based on Specialist applications and Construction valuations within time limits that correspond to the equivalent time limits in clause 20 of the PPC2000

Partnering Terms (20.3, 20.5, 20.12, 20.13). The Specialist has an obligation to pay all Sub-Specialists the amounts to which they are entitled, to maintain full records of all amounts payable and paid, and to make these available to the Constructor on request (20.10).

Clause 21   **Specialist Completion and Support**

The relevant time limits in this clause are seven (7) Working Days' (or otherwise as stated in the Specialist Works Brief) notice of Specialist Completion and four (4) Working Days following attendance, inspection and testing for Constructor confirmation as to whether Specialist Completion has been achieved (21.1, 21.2).

Clause 22   **Duty of Care and Warranties**

This clause reflects equivalent duties of care to those expressed in clause 22 of the PPC2000 Partnering Terms and extends the requirement for direct warranties in favour of the Client to pick up those offered by or otherwise available from particular Sub-Specialists.

Clause 23   **Specialist KPIs and Continuous Improvement**

This clause provides for review of performance against Specialist KPIs, to be undertaken by the Constructor and the Specialist by reference to such information as is reasonably necessary to demonstrate progress (23.1). This clause also provides for the Constructor and Specialist to attend a meeting after Specialist Completion to review performance against the Specialist KPIs and to consider the scope for further improvement on future projects (23.3).

Clause 24   **Joint Initiatives and Strategic Alliancing**

This clause recognises the potential for agreement of joint initiatives and strategic alliancing relationships, subject to performance against the Specialist KPIs and agreement of specific terms consistent with current applicable laws and regulations.

Clause 25   **General**

This clause contains general provisions equivalent to those in clause 25 of the PPC2000 Partnering Terms.

Clause 26   **Termination**

Clause 26.1 provides the Constructor with a right of termination for non-achievement of agreed pre-conditions to implementation of the Specialist Works, and also in the event of termination under clause 26.1 of the PPC2000 Partnering Terms of the relevant PPC2000 Partnering Contract. It requires the Constructor to notify the Specialist of the date and reason for termination under clause 26.1 of the PPC2000 Partnering Terms within five (5) Working Days following receipt of notice under that clause.

The remainder of this clause provides for termination in the event of bankruptcy, insolvency or Constructor or Specialist breach (26.2, 26.3, 26.5). Clause 26.4 sets out agreed arrangements following termination for Specialist insolvency,

GUIDE to PPC2000 & SPC2000   © ACA and Trowers & Hamlins 2003

bankruptcy or breach, entitling the Constructor to complete the Specialist Works using others and to recover consequent additional cost from the Specialist, entitling the Constructor and other Partnering Team members and Other Specialists to use temporary buildings, plant, tools, materials, goods and equipment intended for (or for use in connection with) the Specialist Works and delivered to Site, and entitling the Constructor to instruct the Specialist to remove any such items and otherwise itself to remove and sell any such items (26.4(i), (ii)). It also requires the Specialist to assign, if so required by the Constructor, the benefit of any agreement for the supply of materials, goods or equipment or for the execution of any works or services for the purpose of the Specialist Works, to the extent that they are assignable and to the extent permitted by law (26.4(iii)). It also entitles the Constructor to pay any Sub-Specialist for any materials, goods or equipment delivered to Site or any work or services executed for the purposes of the Specialist Works, where delivered or executed prior to termination of the Specialist's appointment, to the extent not already paid for and to the extent permitted by law (26.4 (iv)).

The clause recognises that termination of the appointment of the Constructor under the Partnering Contract will automatically trigger termination of the Specialist's appointment, and describes arrangements following such termination or following termination of the Specialist's appointment due to Constructor bankruptcy, insolvency or breach (26.6, 26.7).

Clause 27 **Problem-Solving and Dispute Avoidance or Resolution**

This clause identifies a *"Specialist difference or dispute"* and provides for its resolution in accordance with the relevant PPC2000 Partnering Contract where the Specialist is a Partnering Team member (27.1). Otherwise, the clause provides for alternative dispute resolution options equivalent to those set out in clause 27 of the PPC2000 Partnering Terms.

Clause 28 **Specialist Special Terms**

This clause provides for Specialist Special Terms to be set out in or attached to the Specialist Agreement. These should reflect any Special Terms in the relevant PPC2000 Partnering Contract, and any additional Specialist Special Terms appropriate to the relationship between the Constructor and the Specialist.

CHAPTER 8 - SCOTTISH SUPPLEMENT PPC(S)2000

8.1 INTRODUCTION

Although PPC2000 is designed to be applied to any type of partnered project in any jurisdiction, the Partnering Team members should ensure that PPC2000 and the other Partnering Documents are consistent with all laws and regulations governing the Partnering Contract, namely those of the country stated in the Project Partnering Agreement, and also those currently in force in the country in which the Site is located. Advice on these matters should be obtained from the Partnering Adviser.

In order to facilitate the use of PPC2000 for partnered projects in Scotland governed by Scottish law, the ACA has produced a Scottish Supplement PPC(S)2000 with advice from Scottish lawyers Brechin Tindal Oatts.

8.2 STRUCTURE

The Scottish Supplement PPC(S)2000 introduces variations to PPC2000 to reflect the requirements of Scottish law and to provide for attestation in accordance with Scottish law. It is a brief document that should be attached to the relevant PPC2000 Project Partnering Agreement, and both documents should be completed and agreed.

It is also advised that, when completing the two documents together, Partnering Team members should ensure that the following is written on the front cover of the completed PPC2000 Project Partnering Agreement: *"This is the Project Partnering Agreement and Partnering Terms referred to in the Scottish Supplement (PPC(S)2000) entered into by [*insert names of Partnering Team members]"*.

8.3 CONTENTS

Scottish Supplement PPC(S)2000 comprises a supplementary Project Partnering Agreement which recites details of the Project and Site and records the agreement of the parties to implement the Partnering Contract subject to listed variations necessary to achieve compliance with Scottish governing law.

The listed amendments include the following:-

- Deletion of the option to execute PPC2000 documents as deeds, as the concept of execution by deed is not applicable in Scotland;

- Replacement of the word *"assignment"* with the word *"assignation"*, which is the equivalent term under Scottish law;

- Replacement of the word *"arbitrator"* with the word *"arbiter"*, which is the equivalent term under Scottish law;

- Insertion of a new clause recording the consent of the Partnering Team members to registration of the Partnering Documents for preservation and execution;

- Deletion of a number of words used in relation to insolvency and bankruptcy, and their replacement with appropriate equivalent terms under Scottish law;

- Creation of new attestation clauses for all PPC2000 Agreements to provide for signature in accordance with Scottish law;

- Amendment of the arbitration provisions to exclude operation of Section 3 of the Administration of Justice (Scotland) Act 1972.

GUIDE to PPC2000 & SPC2000   © ACA and Trowers & Hamlins 2003

CHAPTER 9 - PARTNERING ADVISER

9.1 WHAT IS THE PARTNERING ADVISER?

The CIC Partnering Task Force recognised that the promotion of partnered relationships and processes would not be sufficient alone to change ingrained, adversarial ways of working. Without the availability of ongoing advice and support, it is difficult to expect Partnering Team members to change the habits of a lifetime, particularly when tackling the practical tensions and crises that are likely to arise at some point in the life of any Project.

Partnering Team members can always obtain advice individually from lawyers and other advisers, but advice obtained by one party alone will be for the benefit of that party alone and may not take full account of the new ways of working that are required for successful partnering. Over-zealous advice that protects one Partnering Team member to the detriment of the others can damage the balance and enthusiasm of the Partnering Team as a whole.

The CIC Guide therefore recommends the appointment of a Partnering Adviser *"to facilitate the smooth creation and development of the project partnering team"*, and for this purpose to:-

" -   *Guide in the selection and partnering process;*

-        *Assist in team building;*

-        *Record and document the project partnering team relationships, commitments made by each party and their expectations in a multi-party partnering contract;*

-        *Provide a first port of call in the event of misunderstandings or disagreements between project partnering team members."*

The role of a Partnering Adviser is distinct from that of a Facilitator, which the CIC Guide describes as *"An external consultant engaged after the Project Partnering Team has been formed to run team-building workshops at key stages in the partnering process".*

9.2 WHAT IS THE PARTNERING ADVISER'S ROLE UNDER PPC2000?

In line with the recommendations in the CIC Guide, PPC2000 proposes the appointment of a Partnering Adviser. It provides in clause 5.6 of the Partnering Terms for the Partnering Team members together or individually to utilise the advice and support of a Partnering Adviser, subject to prior agreement of costs and the Partnering Adviser's duty of care.

The range of the Partnering Adviser's advice and support, set out in clause 5.6 of the PPC2000 Partnering Terms, includes:

"-   *selection of Partnering Team members, team-building and review of Specialist Contracts for consistency with the Partnering Documents;*

-        *preparation of the Project Partnering Agreement and preparation of any Partnering Charter;*

-        *preparation of any Joining Agreements, Pre-Possession Agreement and Commencement Agreement;*

- *provision of fair and constructive advice as to the partnering process, the development of the partnering relationships and the operation of the Partnering Contract;*

- *attendance at such meetings of the Core Group and the Partnering Team as their members consider appropriate;*

- *assistance in the solving of problems and the avoidance or resolution of disputes in accordance with clause 27."*

9.3 WHAT IS THE BENEFIT OF A PARTNERING ADVISER?

The role of the Partnering Adviser is to help in selection and build-up of the Partnering Team, to ensure that the Project Partnering Agreement and all subsequent agreements are concluded correctly, completely and without delay, and to provide whatever support is required to ensure that such documents and the new relationships and processes that they create are fully understood and are fully implemented.

Proper use of a Partnering Adviser should significantly reduce the need for individual Partnering Team members to refer the Partnering Contract to their separate advisers. It enables them together to rely on an independent party outside the Partnering Team who has relevant expertise and who owes a duty of care to all of them. This should save both time and money in achieving rapid conclusion of a mutually agreed contract structure that reflects the common interest of the Partnering Team members .

The amount of work required will vary according to the experience of the Partnering Team members. However, the role of the Partnering Adviser should not be taken over by one confident and experienced Partnering Team member as this will only increase an imbalance with the level of confidence and experience of other Partnering Team members. Although it may not be immediately apparent, the domination of the Partnering Team by one of its members, if the Partnering Adviser is absent or is not invited to perform his or her proper role, can significantly undermine the mutual trust and co-operation necessary to get the best out of the partnering relationships and processes.

Accordingly, whenever a Partnering Team works together for the first time, or whenever an additional member is added for the first time, it is important to allow the Partnering Adviser to fulfil all of the functions described in the CIC Guide and in clause 5.6 of the PPC2000 Partnering Terms. On subsequent Projects, economies can be achieved as regards the level of advice and support from the Partnering Adviser if all Partnering Team members so agree.

In all cases, the intention is that a Partnering Adviser will reduce rather than increase the need and cost of independent advice, by means of:-

- Avoiding or at least deferring the need for individual Partnering Team members to obtain their own separate advice and support, with the risk of duplication and the risk of delay while differences are resolved or negotiated;

- By providing the Partnering Team members with confidence in and understanding of the Partnering Contract so that they will operate it as a self-sustaining Partnering Team from the earliest opportunity, and as a consequence will be able to mitigate problems and resolve potential differences or disputes.

GUIDE to PPC2000 & SPC2000   © ACA and Trowers & Hamlins 2003

9.4 WHO IS A SUITABLE PARTNERING ADVISER?

To quote from the CIC Guide *"The partnering adviser can come from any suitable discipline, but his or her skills set must be right for the role and the proposed project"*.

The Partnering Adviser should be an individual with experience appropriate to the needs of the Partnering Team and the Project.

In accordance with the recommendations of the CIC Guide, the Partnering Adviser should be independent from and acceptable to all Partnering Team members. In practice, the Partnering Adviser may be recommended by one or more Partnering Team members on the basis of his or her reputation and previous work. As in the selection of the Partnering Team members themselves, prior knowledge of the Partnering Adviser is a preferable basis to establish the personal trust and confidence necessary for proper fulfilment of his or her functions. In any event, the Partnering Team members should make a selection that is acceptable to all of them, and under clause 5.7 of the PPC2000 Partnering Terms the Core Group may replace the Partnering Adviser at any time.

There exists an Association of Partnering Advisers (the *"APA"*) which provides accreditation for Partnering Advisers and collates details of their particular experience. The APA database can be used as a means for Project Partnering Teams to select a Partnering Adviser who is appropriate to their Project and their other requirements.

The APA Code of Conduct for Members requires that members should have *"adequate resources and experienced personnel"*, should *"be supported by insurance in respect of their own and their organisation's liability"* and should set out in writing their terms of appointment, including:-

- The scope of their services;

- Their responsibilities and any limit of liability;

- The method of calculation and timing of payment of their remuneration;

- Provisions for termination of their appointment.

The APA requires that any member *"shall at all times act impartially as a Partnering Adviser and shall fully co-operate with such other parties to the Project and pay due regard to the statutory obligations and qualifications of all other parties associated with the Project"*.

Members are required to have no function within the Partnering Contract or Project concerned other than that of Partnering Adviser, or to have any other conflict of interest, and are required to disclose to any prospective client any existing or potential conflict of interest which might give rise to doubts as to their ability or integrity to make independent judgements as a Partnering Adviser.

For further details of the APA and the conditions of membership, please contact the ACA at the address printed on the inside front cover of this guide.

To quote again from the CIC Guide *"Initially and importantly there must be commitment and trust in the relationship between the client and the partnering adviser and this trust must be carried through in the relationships with the appointed partnering team members"*.

9.5   SHOULD THE PARTNERING ADVISER BE A PARTNERING TEAM MEMBER?

PPC2000 does not provide for the Partnering Adviser to be a member of the Partnering Team, for the following reasons:-

- To ensure that the Partnering Adviser can provide independent advice and support by reference to the Partnering Contract, without the potential conflict of interest that would arise if the Partnering Adviser was a party to that Contract, with its own contractual rights and obligations to protect;

- So that the Partnering Team members have maximum flexibility in their use of the Partnering Adviser's advice and support pursuant to clause 5.6 of the PPC2000 Partnering Terms;

- So that the Core Group can, if necessary, replace the Partnering Adviser in accordance with clause 5.7 of the PPC2000 Partnering Terms without first having to implement contractual termination provisions in respect of the original Partnering Adviser's appointment.

The CIC Guide states that *"The partnering adviser would not be a party to the partnering contract"*. It also states that *"It is imperative that the partnering adviser is not the client's representative, as trust within the project partnering team will be threatened if the adviser is not regarded as an independent authority with an interest in the success of the project as a whole"*.

GUIDE to PPC2000 & SPC2000   © ACA and Trowers & Hamlins 2003

CHAPTER 10 - PPC2000 IN USE

TEN COMMON PITFALLS

10.1 WHAT IS HAPPENING IN PRACTICE?

PC2000 has been used for the procurement of a wide variety of individual Projects and strategic programmes, spanning the public, voluntary and private sectors. Most PPC2000 Projects report considerable success in meeting and exceeding agreed KPI targets, including those for reduced cost and time and for improved quality and profitability: some of these are Demonstration Projects registered with Rethinking Construction and many have been subject to independent review or audit of their achievements.

However, PPC2000 cannot assist Partnering Teams who do not give serious thought to the best way in which its provisions should be put into effect. PPC2000 offers considerable flexibility in the agreement of processes for design development, risk management, supply chain build-up and finalisation of prices. This flexibility invites Partnering Team members to think through how they wish to implement these processes and what will best serve their respective interests and those of the Project itself.

The issues are those that an effective Partnering Team will wish to clarify in any event, and to embody them in the PPC2000 Partnering Contract provides a route map for forward-planning.

10.2 WHAT GOES WRONG AND WHY?

Where problems arise, they frequently result from one of the following ten common pitfalls of Project partnering:-

10.2.1 The Client is not actively involved as a Partnering Team member

PPC2000 does not require the Client to take over any other Partnering Team member's role or responsibilities. It allows the Client Representative to represent the Client in all matters other than membership of the Core Group.

However, in practice if the Client does not take an active interest in the Project, this will encourage cynicism and apathy amongst other Partnering Team members as to the level of the Client's genuine commitment to Project partnering.

This apparent lack of committment can lead other Partnering Team members to believe that their ideas for innovation or their Early Warning as to problems will not reach the Client, but only the Client Representative, and this in turn can limit or discourage trust and openness.

10.2.2 Any Partnering Team member is not committed to change

Project partnering still represents a major departure from ways of working that are widely familiar in the construction industry. All Partnering Team members (the Client, Constructor, Consultants and Specialists) need to be committed to changing those ways of working, and PPC2000 clarifies how they should achieve this.

If any Partnering Team member, or for that matter any individual representing a Partnering Team member, is not committed to such change, their attitude can undermine effective Project partnering. If one Partnering Team member is actively searching for claims, differences and disputes, then other Partnering Team members will be more likely to take a defensive or aggressive stance, and the claims, differences and disputes will be much more likely to arise.

10.2.3 Failure to select the Constructor and Specialists early

One of the key innovations of PPC2000 is to establish an integrated set of contractual relationships and processes during the pre-construction phase of the Project prior to start on Site. Postponement of signature of the Project Partnering Agreement shortens this pre-construction phase and delays full involvement of the Constructor and key Specialists.

The Constructor and Specialists can only make significant design contributions, and put forward other innovative ideas for reduced cost and time or improved quality, if:-

- The Constructor is appointed at the start of a sufficient pre-construction phase;

- There is an agreed basis during the pre-construction phase for Specialists to contribute to design development, either before or after their formal selection.

10.2.4 Failure to complete the Partnering Timetable

The Partnering Timetable is essential to clarify the activities and interfaces of Partnering Team members during the pre-construction phase *(see also Chapter 5.7)*. It provides a project management tool that acts as a driver for progress during the pre-construction phase.

If the Partnering Timetable is not created and signed at the same time as the Project Partnering Agreement, then there is a serious risk that delays will occur in key activities during the pre-construction phase. If Partnering Team members cannot rely on each other to meet agreed deadlines, then the partnering relationships may be seriously threatened.

10.2.5 Failure to clarify and integrate the Project Brief, Project Proposals and Consultant Services Schedules

These documents describe what the Client requires from the Project and the ways in which the Constructor, Consultants and Specialists will respond to those requirements (see also Chapter 5). If these Partnering Documents are not drawn up carefully and in sufficient detail, there will be the risk of:-

- Gaps in agreed activities, leading to delays and potential disputes if required works or services are not performed;

- Duplication in agreed activities, leading to wasted money and confusion as to which Partnering Team member is responsible for what;

GUIDE to PPC2000 & SPC2000   © ACA and Trowers & Hamlins 2003

- Problems of communication and mutual reliance between Partnering Team members if the interfaces between their respective roles and responsibilities are not clearly defined.

10.2.6 Lack of interest in Specialist sub-contractors and suppliers

The build-up and integration of the supply chain on the basis of agreed selection processes during the pre-construction phase is a significant change. Under the traditional construction industry approach, the Constructor relies primarily on its estimators and on informal sub-contractor/supplier quotes during the pre-construction phase, and formalises most of these arrangements during the construction phase. To move away from the traditional approach requires considerable effort and organisation, particularly on the part of the Constructor, and this needs to be supported and facilitated by other Partnering Team members.

If there is an insufficient pre-construction phase, or if the Partnering Timetable does not recognise sufficient periods for selection of Specialist sub-contractors and suppliers at appropriate stages, then key benefits will be lost in terms of Specialist design input, improved cost certainty and removal of contingencies to cover the risk of Specialist price movements.

10.2.7 KPIs and incentives are not agreed early

PPC2000 provides for the provisional agreement of KPIs and related targets at the point of signing the Project Partnering Agreement and for these to be firmed up not later than the date of the Commencement Agreement. It is important to record clearly the consequences of Partnering Team members exceeding, meeting or failing to meet agreed KPI targets, particularly where these consequences act as incentives to improved performance.

If KPIs are neglected or targets are not agreed or related incentives are not put in place, this will reduce the motivation of Partnering Team members.

10.2.8 Joint risk management is neglected

Another key benefit of the pre-construction phase under PPC2000 is the opportunity for the Partnering Team members jointly to analyse and manage risks with a view to removing or reducing any prospective risk contingencies included by the Constructor in the original Price Framework. If the pre-construction phase is too short or if the risk analysis and management process is neglected, this can lead to risks being transferred rather than managed. If there are no agreed means to eliminate, reduce, insure, share or apportion risks on a mutually agreed basis, then risks transferred to the Constructor will be priced by the Constructor. Risk pricing in this way is a gamble for both the Client and the Constructor as to whether the risk premium is too high (i.e. wasted money) or too low (i.e. insufficient to cover the Constructor's actual costs). Not only is this approach a missed opportunity for a more scientific approach to the relevant risks, but it also imposes considerable strains on other aspects of the partnering relationships.

10.2.9 Failure to appoint and use an appropriate independent Partnering Adviser

The role and functions of the Partnering Adviser, and the reasons for using a Partnering Adviser as an independent source of guidance and experience, are described in Chapter 9.

If the Partnering Adviser is not independent (for example if he or she is an employee of the Client or Client Representative or Constructor), then this can undermine the confidence of other Partnering Team members in the establishment of a fair and balanced set of relationships and processes.

If the Partnering Adviser is not suitably experienced, then this can lead to errors in the Partnering Contract and a lack of focus and momentum in supporting and driving forward the PPC2000 partnering processes.

10.2.10 Failure to read PPC2000

PPC2000 may not be the favourite reading material of Partnering Team members, but it is an accessible, reasonably concise document that applies equally to all Partnering Team members. It is a means by which each Partnering Team member can readily identify not only its own role and responsibilities, but also those of all other Partnering Team members, and can see how these inter-relate throughout the pre-construction phase and construction phase of the Project.

If Partnering Team members do not read the Partnering Contract that they have created, then it will be difficult for them to understand clearly the roles and relationships that they have established and the processes that they have agreed to follow. In practice, lack of familiarity with these roles, relationships and processes leads to traditional adversarial alternatives being put into practice. This disparity causes confusion and a much greater likelihood of differences and disputes.

PPC2000 PROJECT PARTNERING AGREEMENT CHECKLIST
(For review by all Partnering Team members with advice from the Partnering Adviser)
(see also Chapter 4.3)

Check

1.   CONTENTS

Clauses 1.3, 1.5,
1.6 and 10.2

Partnering Team Members

Are there clearly identified the Client and Constructor and all other signatories to the Project Partnering Agreement with relevant contact details and an agreed basis for execution of the Project Partnering Agreement?

Does the Partnering Team include all appropriate Partnering Team members under the categories of Consultant and Specialist? Have Consultant Service Schedules and Consultant Payment Terms been agreed? *(See also Chapter 5).* Have Specialist Contracts been agreed? *(See also Chapter 7).*

Clause 2

Project Brief, Project Proposals, Price Framework

Have there been prepared and agreed suitable forms of Project Brief, Project Proposals and Price Framework appropriate for signature with the Project Partnering Agreement? *(See also Chapter 5).* Does the terminology in these documents correspond to that in PPC2000?

Clause 2

KPIs

Have the Partnering Team members agreed KPIs and related targets? If these are provisional, does the Partnering Timetable indicate how they will be developed or firmed up? Are there KPIs for all Partnering Team members? Do the KPIs state clearly the agreed consequences of exceeding, meeting or failing to meet agreed KPI targets?

Clause 2

Partnering Timetable

Is there a Partnering Timetable that covers all agreed activities and interfaces and that is consistent with PPC2000? *(See also Chapter 5).* Does it provide for each activity to be the responsibility of a specified Partnering Team member, with clear periods of time for each activity so that each Partnering Team member's role and responsibilities interlocks clearly with those of the other Partnering Team members? Are there the necessary periods for design development and for Business Case preparation, tendering and pricing in relation to each works or services package, with all appropriate approvals and with arrangements for maximum early Constructor and Specialist design input? Does the Partnering Timetable recognise the possible impact of matters outside the Partnering Team members' control? Are there agreed periods for Risk Management, Value Management and Value Engineering exercises? Is there provision for partnering workshops?

Clause 3.3

Core Group

Are the Core Group members the right individuals to work as a cohesive group? *(See also Appendix 5).* Have they been made aware of their responsibilities and do they have appropriate experience? Are Core Group meetings specified in the Partnering Timetable? Is it appropriate to have alternate Core Group members?

Clause 3.9

Interested Parties

Have the Partnering Team members agreed appropriate Interested Parties and stated what documents they should receive from whom, what meetings they should be invited to and what other entitlements they have?

Check

Clause 5.2 **Client Representative**

Have there been stated against clause 5.2 in the Project Partnering Agreement appropriate restrictions on the authority of the Client Representative? *(See also Appendix 6).*

Clause 5.6 **Partnering Adviser**

Has a Partnering Adviser been appointed who is acceptable to all current Partnering Team members? Is there sufficient understanding as to his or her role and responsibilities and as to his or her duty of care and fees? *(See also Chapter 9 and Appendix 7).*

Clause 8 **Design**

Has there been agreed a Lead Designer and arrangements for any agreed changes in that role during the pre-construction phase and construction phase of the Project?

Have all Design Team members been named or (if not yet selected) described by reference to their professional disciplines or trades?

Clauses 8.3 and 8.6 Has there been stated any amendment agreed to the design development process described in clause 8 of the Partnering Terms? *(See also Appendix 10 Flowchart C).*

Clause 8.4 **Site Surveys and Investigations**

Have all completed Site surveys and investigations and their results been incorporated or described in the Project Brief or Project Proposals?

Have the Partnering Team members agreed what further Site surveys and investigations are required and who will commission and undertake them and with the support of what warranties in favour of which Partnering Team members?

Clauses 1.6 and 10.11 **Client-appointed Specialists**

Will the Client appoint any Specialists direct, are they clearly described and have their terms of appointment been agreed and integrated where necessary with the Partnering Contract?

Clause 13.2 **Shared Savings/Added Value Incentives**

Have the Partnering Team agreed and described clearly their proposed incentive arrangements, in particular as to shared savings and/or shared added value? Have they stated what qualifies as a saving or as added value and how and when it will be distributed?

Clauses 19.3 and 19.4 **Insurances**

Have the agreed levels of third party liability insurance and professional indemnity/product liability insurance of each Partnering Team member been stated? Is it stated whether these amounts relate to each and every event, or each and every claim, or relevant amounts in the aggregate?

Clause 20.9 **Interest on Late Payment**

Is the agreed rate of interest compliant with the Late Payment Act?

Check

Clause 20.13   **<u>Statutory Deduction</u>**

Is the Client a *"contractor"* for the purposes of the ICTA?

Clause 21   **<u>Defects</u>**

Is there an appropriate Defects Liability Period and are there appropriate time limits for rectification of different categories of defect?

Clause 22   **<u>Duty of Care</u>**

Have appropriate deletions/statements been made by reference to clause 22 to clarify the duty of care of each Partnering Team member?

Is it appropriate to create any other amended duties of care or warranties, or to create third party rights under the Contracts (Rights of Third Parties) Act 1999?

As regards the duty of care owed by or to parties outside the Partnering Team (e.g. funders/purchasers/Specialists who do not become Partnering Team members), has it been agreed who will provide/receive collateral warranties and in what form?

Clause 25.2   **<u>Rights of Assignment</u>**

Is it agreed which Partnering Team members, if any, are entitled to assign all or any of their rights and obligations under the Partnering Contract?

Clauses 25 and 27   **<u>Law, Jurisdiction and Dispute Avoidance or Resolution</u>**

What is the agreed applicable law and jurisdiction governing the Partnering Contract?

Who is an appropriate conciliator and who is an appropriate adjudicator, or what are the agreed procedures for their respective appointments, or do the Partnering Team agree the procedures for appointment set out in PPC2000 Appendix 5 Parts 1 and 2?

Is arbitration appropriate?

What is a suitable limitation period for claims and proceedings?

Clause 28   **<u>Special Terms</u>**

Should any Special Terms be added and have these been agreed?

2.   EXECUTION

Have the Partnering Team members agreed to sign the Project Partnering Agreement or to execute it as a deed? Have they all signed or executed it as agreed?

PPC2000 JOINING AGREEMENT CHECKLIST

Check

**(For review by all Partnering Team members, including the Joining Party,
with advice from the Partnering Adviser)**
(See also Chapter 4.4)

1. JOINING PARTY

Is the Joining Party stated as a signatory to the Joining Agreement, with all appropriate contact details?

2. ROLE OF JOINING PARTY

Is the role of the Joining Party clearly described and are there annexed to the Joining Agreement documents that describe its responsibilities and expertise in sufficient detail, and which integrate such role, responsibilities and expertise with those of the other Partnering Team members?

3. INSURANCES

Have the third party liability insurance and professional indemnity/product liability insurance of the Joining Party been stated? Is it stated whether these relate to each and every event, or each and every claim, or relevant amounts in the aggregate?

4. OTHER SIGNATORIES

Are all other Partnering Team members included as signatories to the Joining Agreement?

5. EXECUTION

Is the method of execution of the Joining Agreement the same as that of the Project Partnering Agreement?

GUIDE to PPC2000 & SPC2000   © ACA and Trowers & Hamlins 2003

PPC2000 PRE-POSSESSION AGREEMENT CHECKLIST

(For review by the Client and the Constructor, with advice from the Partnering Adviser)
(See also Chapter 4.5)

Check

1. PRE-POSSESSION ACTIVITIES

Are the Pre-Possession Activities clearly described in terms of their scope and purpose and their relationship to the Project?

Is it stated where the Pre-Possession Activities are described in the Project Brief and Project Proposals and/or how does the Pre-Possession Agreement amend these documents?

2. DATES OF COMPLETION

Is it stated when Pre-Possession Activities are to start, how long they are to continue and when they are to be completed?

Is it stated how these dates and periods fit with the Partnering Timetable, and if and how they may impact on other dates and periods in the Partnering Timetable?

3. PAYMENT

Are there stated the amount or amounts payable for Pre-Possession Activities? Are these broken down with sufficient accuracy, and are the payment stages and arrangements sufficiently clear?

4. OTHER TERMS

Are there are other terms governing Pre-Possession Activities that need to be set out in the Pre-Possession Agreement? For example, are there amendments to the Partnering Terms as they affect Pre-Possession Activities, in particular those listed in clause 13.4 of the Partnering Terms?

5. EXECUTION

Has the Pre-Possession Agreement been signed and dated by the Client and the Constructor?

PPC2000 COMMENCEMENT AGREEMENT CHECKLIST
(For review by all Partnering Team members, with advice from the Partnering Adviser)
(See also Chapter 4.6)

Check

1. GENERAL

Have the Partnering Team members satisfied all pre-conditions to start on Site listed in clause 14.1 of the Partnering Terms, either completely or to such lesser extent as is stated in the Partnering Documents or is otherwise agreed between them?

Are there other pre-conditions to start on Site stated in the Project Brief and have these been similarly satisfied?

To the best of the knowledge of all Partnering Team members, is the Project ready to commence on Site?

2. PROJECT TIMETABLE

Has the Project Timetable been prepared? *(See also Chapter 5.8).* Does it identify all points of interface between Partnering Team members, including for example dates and periods for each release of design information from one Partnering Team member to another, for selection and appointment of any remaining Specialists, for finalisation of outstanding elements of the Agreed Maximum Price and for all required Client approvals?

Does the Project Timetable clearly state the Date of Possession and the Date of Completion?

If the Project is divided into Sections, does the Project Timetable identify all dates and periods relevant to each Section?

Does the Project Timetable clearly state any part or parts of the Site that are in exclusive or non-exclusive possession, by reason of third parties in occupation or otherwise, and any other agreed constraints on Site possession or access? Does it set out agreed procedures for all required notices and programming of relevant activities to take account of these matters, including without limitation any arrangements for deferred possession and interrupted possession of all or any part of the Site?

3. HEALTH AND SAFETY PLAN

Has a Health and Safety Plan been sufficiently developed in compliance with the CDM Regulations and has it been agreed by all Partnering Team members?

4. PROJECT BRIEF AND PROJECT PROPOSALS

Have the Project Brief and Project Proposals been developed and updated to include all current information and supplemental documents, and are the full Project Brief and Project Proposals separately identified and ready for signature as Partnering Documents? *(See also Chapters 5.2 and 5.3).*

5. PRICE

Has the Agreed Maximum Price been agreed and is it supported by a full Price Framework? *(See also Chapter 5.4).*

Have the Partnering Team members considered establishing agreed payment milestones, activity schedules or cashflows as an alternative to the payment arrangements set out in clause 20 of the Partnering Terms?

Does the Price Framework identify clearly all approved prices for Direct Labour Packages, Preferred Specialists and Specialists selected through tender, in each case supported by all relevant pricing details?

GUIDE to PPC2000 & SPC2000   © ACA and Trowers & Hamlins 2003

Check

Does the Price Framework identify any discounts or other benefits payable by any Specialists to the Constructor?

Does the Price Framework identify any provisional sums and the way in which such provisional sums will be dealt with, and does the Project Timetable set out the periods of time and roles and responsibilities of Partnering Team members to achieve this?

Does the Price Framework state clearly whether there is to be any Retention and how and when this is to be released?

6. RISK SHARING

Are any risk sharing arrangements clearly described in the Commencement Agreement? Are these risk sharing arrangements integrated with the Partnering Terms and do they state clearly if and where they amend the Partnering Terms?

7. EXTENSIONS OF TIME

Does the Commencement Agreement state clearly any third party consents entitling a claim for extension of time?

Does the Commencement Agreement state clearly any additional events, beyond those listed in clause 18.3, entitling a claim for extension of time?

Does the Commencement Agreement state clearly any adjusted extensions of time entitling additional Site Overheads?

Does the Commencement Agreement state clearly any adjusted extensions of time entitling a claim for unavoidable work or expenditure?

8. SITE RISK

Does the Commencement Agreement state clearly any exceptions to the Constructor's risk as to the state and condition of the soil and rock strata and any structures and Environment comprising the Site?

9. INSURANCE AND SECURITY

Does the Commencement Agreement state who is to insure the Project and the Site, in whose names such insurance is to be taken out, what waiver of rights of subrogation will apply, what percentage will be added for fees and what additional or adjusted risks will be covered?

Does the Commencement Agreement state whether third party property damage will be covered and if so by whom and in what amount?

Does the Commencement Agreement state whether Environmental Risk Insurance, Latent Defects Insurance or Whole Project Insurance will be applicable and, if so, by whom any of these insurances will be taken out?

Does the Commencement Agreement identify clearly the amount and form of any required advance payment guarantee, performance bond, parent company guarantee or retention bond?

10. PROBLEM-SOLVING HIERARCHY

Is there annexed to the Commencement Agreement an agreed form of Problem-Solving Hierarchy and has it been completed?

11. SPECIAL TERMS

Does the Commencement Agreement include any agreed Special Terms additional to those set out in or attached to the Project Partnering Agreement?

12. EXECUTION

Has the Commencement Agreement been signed and dated by all Partnering Team members?

CORE GROUP CHECKLIST
(For review by all Core Group members, with advice from the Partnering Adviser)

Check

PPC2000 defines the Core Group as *"the individuals identified in the Project Partnering Agreement as Core Group members, subject only in each case to replacement in accordance with the Partnering Terms, and so that references shall apply to each and all Core Group members"*. It describes in clause 3.3 of the Partnering Terms the essential function of the Core Group to *"meet regularly to review and stimulate the progress of the Project and the implementation of the Partnering Contract and to fulfil their other functions as described in these Partnering Terms"*.

Under clause 3.4 of the Partnering Terms, each Partnering Team member must ensure that any of its employees who are Core Group members attend Core Group meetings and fulfil the agreed functions of a Core Group member in accordance with the Partnering Documents. Although Core Group members are named in the Project Partnering Agreement, they do not under PPC2000 acquire personal liability, and it is the Partnering Team member that is the employer of a Core Group member that is responsible for his or her actions in accordance with clause 7.4 of the Partnering Terms.

Consultation	As regards to all functions of the Core Group that involve Consultation, this is defined in Appendix 1 as *"such consultation as shall be reasonable without delaying the Project and without delaying any necessary action of any Partnering Team member for the benefit of the Project"*.
Consensus	Decisions of Core Group are to be *"by Consensus of all of those Core Group members present at that meeting"*.
	Consensus is defined in Appendix 1 as *"unanimous agreement following reasoned discussion"*.
	In the event of failure by the Core Group to reach Consensus on any matter, other contractual provisions in the Partnering Documents will be the basis for dealing with the relevant matter by reference to the agreed role, expertise and responsibilities of each Partnering Team member.
Early Warning *Clause 3.7*	In the event of Early Warning of any matter adversely affecting or threatening the Project or a Partnering Team member's performance, the Core Group meet to review proposals for avoiding or remedying such matter and agree an appropriate course of action, unless they can agree such course of action without a meeting.
	If the Core Group do not agree a course of action, the Partnering Team members rely solely on their contractual roles, expertise and responsibilities in dealing with the relevant matter.
Value Engineering Value Management and Risk Management *Clause 5.1 (iii)*	The Core Group are to consider proposals based on the results of Value Engineering, Value Management and Risk Management exercises. In the event of non-approval, such proposals are not implemented.
Constructor non-compliance with instructions *Clause 5.5*	There should be Core Group Consultation before the Client acts on Constructor's failure to carry out an instruction under clause 5.5. This operates as a brake on unilateral Client action.
Replacement of individuals *Clause 7.5*	There should be Core Group Consultation prior to Client exclusion of any individual disrupting or adversely affecting the Project. This operates as a brake on unilateral Client action.
Design and process development *Clause 8*	There should be Core Group Consultation throughout the design process in respect of each set of designs submitted, before they are presented for Client approval. This is key to consultative design development. Client approval is the final determinant at each stage.

GUIDE to PPC2000 & SPC2000   © ACA and Trowers & Hamlins 2003

		Check
Analysis of Business Cases *Clause 10.4*	There should be Core Group Consultation in respect of supply chain Business Cases. Client approval under Clause 10.5 is the final determinant.	
Specialist Tenders *Clause 10.6*	There should be Core Group Consultation as to tender returns from prospective Specialists. Client approval under Clause 10.6 is the final determinant.	
Cost Savings and Added Value *Clause 12.10*	The Core Group should investigate the potential for cost savings/added value. If Core Group fail to investigate or agree, then Partnering Team members will not benefit from such cost savings or added value arrangements.	
Incentives *Clause 13.1*	The Core Group should consider and seek to agree incentives additional to those set out in Partnering Documents. If the Core Group fail to agree, then additional incentives will not be created.	
Shared Savings and Added Value Arrangements *Clause 13.2*	The Core Group should consider and recommend to the Client shared savings arrangements and added value incentives additional to those described in the Project Partnering Agreement. If the Core Group fail to consider or agree, then the Partnering Team members will not benefit from such additional shared savings arrangements or added value incentives.	
Payment and KPIs *Clause 13.5*	The Core Group should determine additional or reduced payments resulting from any agreed links between payment and achievement of KPI targets. If the Core Group fail to agree, then the addition or reduction will not be made.	
Operation *Clause 21.6*	The Core Group should consider with the Client proposals submitted by Partnering Team members for Operation of the completed Project.	
KPIs *Clause 23*	The Core Group should review performance of all Partnering Team members by reference to agreed KPIs, should consider and seek to agree measures as necessary to remedy failure to achieve KPI targets, should investigate proposals for continuous improvement and may recommend revision of the criteria for continuous improvement as set out in the KPIs. If the Core Group fail to agree on any of these matters, no further action will be taken in respect of that matter.	
Termination *Clauses 26.3, 26.4 and 26.5*	Proposed termination of any Partnering Team member's appointment for breach should follow 10 Working Days for Core Group Consultation. This operates as a brake on unilateral action. If no Core Group solution is agreed, then termination proceeds.	
Suspension/ abandonment *Clause 26.6*	In the event of impossibility to proceed with or complete the Project, a meeting of the Core Group should consider the problem and any possible solution - but unless the Core Group recommends and the Client approves such a solution, then suspension or abandonment will proceed.	
Difference or Dispute *Clause 27.3*	Where the Problem-Solving Hierarchy does not achieve a negotiated solution, a difference or dispute should be referred to a meeting of the Core Group who should make constructive proposals with a view to negotiating and agreeing an appropriate solution. If no Core Group solution is agreed, then the problem will be referred to other mechanisms for solving problems or avoiding or resolving disputes.	

CLIENT REPRESENTATIVE CHECKLIST

Check

General   PPC2000 provides for the Client Representative, as a party to the Partnering Contract, to fulfil the role and responsibilities described in the Partnering Documents.

Clause 5.1 of the Partnering Terms provides that the Client Representative shall :-

- fulfill its functions as described in the Partnering Terms and other Partnering Documents (and it is envisaged that these will be clarified in a Consultant Services Schedule for the Client Representative);

- exercise any discretion fairly and constructively;

- facilitate an integrated design, supply and construction process in accordance with the Partnering Documents and with the support of other Partnering Team members as stated in the Partnering Documents;

- call, organise, attend and minute Core Group meetings and Partnering Team meetings (and chair Partnering Team meetings unless those present agree otherwise);

- organise and monitor contributions of Partnering Team members to Value Engineering, Value Management and Risk Management exercises and submit to the Client and Core Group proposals for approval based on the results of these exercises and in the best interests of the Project;

- organise partnering workshops in accordance with the Partnering Timetable and as otherwise required by the Core Group;

- monitor implementation of the Project on and off Site with the support of other Partnering Team members as stated in the Partnering Documents.

Authority   The Client Representative, under clause 5.2 of the Partnering Terms, is authorised to represent the Client in all matters relating to the Project except membership of the Core Group.

The authority of the Client Representative is subject only to such restrictions as are stated in the Project Partnering Agreement (by reference to clause 5.2 of the Partnering Terms). It is essential that any restrictions (e.g. as to entitlement to vary time, cost or quality) are clearly stated so that all Partnering Team members are aware of them. The authority of the Client Representative is also subject to the procedures stated in the Partnering Documents.

Under clauses 5.3, 5.4 and 5.5 of the Partnering Terms the Client Representative has the authority to issue instructions to the Constructor in accordance with the Partnering Documents *"Where necessary and without prejudicing the collaborative spirit of the partnering relationships"*.

GUIDE to PPC2000 & SPC2000   © ACA and Trowers & Hamlins 2003

Check

It is important to note that in the exercise of all its functions under the Partnering Contract, the Client Representative must exercise its judgement by reference to the Partnering Documents and the facts of the situation. None of the Client Representative's functions are dependent on the subjective exercise of the Client Representative's judgement, as in all cases such judgement can be challenged by relevant Partnering Team members through specific provisions of the PPC2000 Partnering Terms. See for example clauses 5.4, 17.4, 18.4, 20.7 and 20.16.

Specialists

In relation to the appointment of Specialists, the Client Representative is entitled to receive copies of all relevant documentation and to attend all interviews and other meetings with prospective Specialists, as stated in clause 10.7 of the Partnering Terms.

Change

Under clause 17.4 of the Partnering Terms, if the Client and Constructor do not agree the time and/or cost of proposals set out in a Constructor's Change Submission, then the Client Representative is required within a 20 Working Day period to ascertain the time and cost effects of such Change on a fair and reasonable basis utilising wherever possible relevant periods of time in the Partnering Timetable and Project Timetable and prices for similar work in the Price Framework. *(See also Appendix 10 Flowchart (F)).*

Time/Cost

Under clause 18.4 of the Partnering Terms, in response to Constructor notification of an agreed event giving rise to an extension of time and/or unavoidable work or expenditure, the Client Representative is required to respond to the Constructor's proposals to minimise adverse effects within 2 Working Days and to respond to the Constructor's notification of time and cost consequences within 20 Working Days. The Client Representative may request reasonable additional information to support the Constructor's submission.

The Client Representative is required to ascertain a fair and reasonable extension of time taking into account the Project Timetable and to ascertain any additional Site Overheads in accordance with clause 18.5 and any other fair and reasonable increase with the Agreed Maximum Price in accordance with clause 18.6, taking into account the Price Framework. *(See also Appendix 10 Flowchart (G)).*

Valuations

Under clause 20 of the Partnering Terms, the Client Representative is required to issue valuations in response to the Constructor's applications for payment and to issue an account and valuations following Project Completion and a Final Account for agreement following satisfaction of the Constructor's defects rectification obligations, each within agreed periods compliant with the Housing Grants, Construction and Regeneration Act 1996. Constructor applications for payment must be accompanied by details as stated in the Price Framework and such further information as the Client Representative may reasonably require.

Project Completion

Under clause 21 of the Partnering Terms, the Client Representative is required to attend, inspect and test in accordance with the agreed arrangements for Project Completion, and to confirm within stated timescales whether Project Completion has been achieved.

Defects Rectification

Under clause 21.5 of the Partnering Terms, the Client Representative is required to issue a notice confirming the date when the Constructor's obligations as to defects rectification have been satisfied.

Duty of Care

Under clause 22 of the Partnering Terms, the duty of care of the Client Representative is that of reasonable skill and care appropriate to its agreed role, expertise and responsibilities as stated in the Partnering Documents, subject to any amendments/restrictions stated in the Project Partnering Agreement. That duty of care is owed to all other Partnering Team members.

Termination

The appointment of the Client Representative under the Partnering Contract may be terminated:-

- by the Client:

  - by notice in the event that prior to signature of the Commencement Agreement the Client (due to non-satisfaction of pre-conditions or for any other unforeseeable reason) no longer wishes to proceed with the Project (clause 26.1); or

  - automatically in the event of the Client Representative's bankruptcy or insolvency (clause 26.2); or

  - by notice, after Core Group Consultation, in the event of the Client Representative's material breach of the Partnering Contract (clause 26.3).

- by the Client Representative:

  - automatically in the event of the Client's bankruptcy or insolvency (clause 26.2); or

  - by notice, after Core Group Consultation, in the event of the Client's specified breach of the Partnering Contract (clause 26.5).

Check

GUIDE to PPC2000 & SPC2000   © ACA and Trowers & Hamlins 2003

PARTNERING ADVISER CHECKLIST

Check

Appointment

Have the Partnering Team members appointed a Partnering Adviser?

Is the Partnering Adviser independent from all Partnering Team members?

Is the Partnering Adviser acceptable to all Partnering Team members?

Fees

Is there a clearly understood arrangement as to the Partnering Adviser's fees, and as to which Partnering Team members will be responsible for their payment?

Duty of Care

Is it clear that the Partnering Adviser owes a duty of care to all Partnering Team members and has this been confirmed by the Partnering Adviser?

Scope of Services

Have there been clarified with the Partnering Adviser the services required in terms of:-

- Selection of Partnering Team members and team-building?

- Preparation of the Project Partnering Agreement, review of other Partnering Documents and preparation of any Partnering Charter?

- Review of Specialist Contracts?

- Preparation of any Joining Agreements, Pre-Possession Agreement and Commencement Agreement?

- Provision of fair and constructive advice and support as to the partnering process, the development of the partnering relationships and the operation of the Partnering Contract?

- Any required attendance at meetings of the Core Group or Partnering Team?

- Any required assistance in the solving of problems and the avoidance or resolution of disputes?

Association of Partnering Advisers

Is the Partnering Adviser a member of the Association of Partnering Advisers?

Is the experience of the Partnering Adviser, as recorded on the Association of Partnering Advisers' database, appropriate to the needs of the Partnering Team and the Project?

PPC2000 TIMESCALES

<u>NOTE:</u>   Those timescales marked * may be varied by prior agreement of the stated Partnering Team or Core Group members.

<u>NOTE:</u>   In addition to the timescales set out below, the Partnering Team members will be bound by the agreed dates and periods of time set out in the Partnering Timetable and Project Timetable respectively.

Clause 3.5	Notice of Core Group meetings – At least five (5) Working Days.*
Clause 3.7	Following Early Warning, Client Representative to convene Core Group meeting - Within five (5) Working Days.*
Clause 3.8	Notice of Partnering Team meetings - At least five (5) Working Days.
Clause 5.4	Objection to Client Representative instruction - Within two (2) Working Days.
Clause 5.4	Following confirmation Client Representative instruction, Constructor implementation of clause 17/18/27 - Within two (2) Working Days.
Clause 5.5	Following Client notice repeating Client Representative instruction, Constructor compliance with instruction - Within five (5) Working Days.
Clause 8.11	Constructor objection to design - Within five (5) Working Days.*
Clause 8.11	Following Lead Designer confirmation/amendment/withdrawal of design, Constructor implementation of clause 17/18/27 - Within two (2) Working Days.
Clause 15.1	Partnering Team members' comments on Commencement Agreement - Within ten (10) Working Days.
Clause 17.2	Following notification of proposed Change, submission of Constructor's Change Submission - Within ten (10) Working Days.*
Clause 17.3	Following Constructor's Change Submission, Client Representative instruction to proceed/withdrawal of Change - Within five (5) Working Days.*
Clause 17.4	Following instruction to proceed, agreement of time/cost effects of Change by reference to Constructor's Change Submission - Within twenty (20) Working Days.
Clause 17.4	Failing agreement, Client Representative notice of time/cost effects of Change - Within twenty (20) Working Days.
Clause 17.4	Following Client Representative notice, Client or Constructor notification as to time/cost effects of Change - Within twenty (20) Working Days.
Clause 18.3(i)	Constructor Early Warning prior to expiry of agreed Client/ Consultant time limit - At least five (5) Working Days.
Clause 18.4(ii)	Client Representative instruction to Constructor by reference to proposals to minimise effects of delay/disruption event - Within two (2) Working Days.
Clause 18.4	Client Representative response to Constructor notification of delay/disruption event - Within twenty (20) Working Days.
Clause 18.4	Following Client Representative response, Client or Constructor notification of dispute as to time/cost effects of delay/disruption event - Within twenty (20) Working Days.
Clause 20.3	Following Constructor application for payment, Client Representative valuation - Within five (5) Working Days.*
Clause 20.3	Constructor payment - Within fifteen (15) Working Days from issue of valuation or ten (10) Working Days from receipt of required VAT invoice, whichever is the later.*
Clause 20.4	Following Consultant application for payment, Client notice - Within fifteen (15) Working Days.*

Clause 20.4	Consultant payment - Within fifteen (15) Working Days from date of Client notice or ten (10) Working Days from receipt of required VAT invoice, whichever is the later.*
Clause 20.6	Latest date, before final date for payment, for notification of withholding or deduction from amount due - Two (2) Working Days.
Clause 20.13	Prior to first application for payment, Constructor evidence of entitlement to be paid without statutory deduction - At least fifteen (15) Working Days.
Clause 20.14	Following Project Completion, Client Representative account - Within twenty (20) Working Days.*
Clause 20.14	Following Project Completion account, Client Representative valuation - Within twenty (20) Working Days.
Clause 20.15	Following satisfaction of defects rectification obligations, Client Representative issue of Final Account - Within twenty (20) Working Days.
Clause 20.16	Following issue of Final Account, Client or Constructor dispute - Within forty (40) Working Days.
Clause 20.17	Notice of proposed suspension of performance for non-payment - At least seven (7) days.
Clause 21.1	Notice of proposed Project Completion - At least five (5) Working Days.*
Clause 21.2	Following attendance/inspection/testing, Client Representative confirmation as to whether Project Completion has been achieved - Within two (2) Working Days.
Clause 26.1	Notice of Client termination of all Partnering Team members' appointments for non-achievement of pre-conditions or for unforeseeable reasons - At least twenty (20) Working Days.
Clause 26.3	Rectification of notified Consultant/Specialist breach - Within ten (10) Working Days.
Clause 26.3	Core Group review of proposed Consultant/ Specialist termination - At least ten (10) Working Days.
Clause 26.4	Rectification of notified Constructor breach - Within ten (10) Working Days.
Clause 26.4	Core Group review of proposed Constructor termination - At least ten (10) Working Days.
Clause 26.5	Rectification of notified Client breach - Within ten (10) Working Days.
Clause 26.5	Core Group review of proposed termination due to Client breach - At least ten (10) Working Days.
Clause 26.5	Valuation following termination for Client breach/insolvency - Within fifteen (15) Working Days.
Clause 26.6	Core Group review of proposed suspension/ abandonment - Within twenty (20) Working Days.
Clause 26.7	Abandonment following suspension - Three (3) calendar months.
Clause 26.10	Notice of Client-appointed Specialist proposed termination of Specialist Contract - At least ten (10) Working Days.
Clause 26.11	Notice of Constructor-appointed Specialist proposed termination of Specialist Contract - At least ten (10) Working Days.
Clause 27.3	Notice of Core Group meeting to review difference or dispute - Maximum ten (10) Working Days.

SPC2000 TIMESCALES

NOTE: Those timescales marked * may be amended by prior agreement between the Constructor and the Specialist.

NOTE: In addition to the following timescales, the Constructor and the Specialist will be bound by the agreed dates and periods of time set out in the Specialist Timetable.

Clause 3.3	Constructor/Specialist meeting following Early Warning - Within five (5) Working Days.
Clause 3.4	Notice of Constructor/Specialist meeting - At least three (3) Working Days.
Clause 5.2	Objection to Constructor instruction - Within two (2) Working Days.
Clause 5.2	Following confirmation/amendment/withdrawal of Constructor instruction, Specialist implementation of clause 17/18/27 - Within two (2) Working Days.
Clause 5.4	Compliance following Constructor notice repeating instruction - Within four (4) Working Days.
Clause 8.8	Specialist objection to design - Within four (4) Working Days.*
Clause 8.8	Following Constructor confirmation/amendment/withdrawal of design, implementation of clause 17/18/27 - Within two (2) Working Days.
Clause 17.2	Following Constructor-proposed Specialist Change, submission of Specialist Change Submission - Within nine (9) Working Days.*
Clause 17.3	Following Specialist Change Submission, Constructor instruction to proceed/ withdrawal of Specialist Change - Within ten (10) Working Days.*
Clause 17.4	Following instruction to proceed, agreement of time/cost effects of Specialist Change - Within fifteen (15) Working Days.
Clause 17.4	Specialist notification of dispute of Constructor notice as to time/cost effects of Specialist Change - Within fifteen (15) Working Days.
Clause 18.3(i)	Specialist Early Warning prior to expiry of agreed Constructor time limit - At least six (6) Working Days.
Clause 18.4(ii)	Constructor instruction by reference to Specialist proposals to minimise effects of delay/disruption event - Within four (4) Working Days.
Clause 18.4	Constructor response to Specialist notification of delay/disruption event - Within twenty-five (25) Working Days.
Clause 18.4	Specialist notification of dispute of Constructor notice as to time/cost effects of delay/disruption event - Within fifteen (15) Working Days.
Clause 20.3	Constructor valuation following Specialist application for payment - Within ten (10) Working Days.*
Clause 20.3	Specialist payment - Within fifteen (15) Working Days from issue of valuation or ten (10) Working Days from receipt of required VAT invoice, whichever is the later.*
Clause 20.5	Latest date, before final date for payment, for notification of withholding or deduction from amount due - Two (2) Working Days.

Clause 20.11	Specialist evidence of entitlement to be paid without statutory deduction, prior to first application for payment - At least fifteen (15) Working Days.
Clause 20.12	Constructor account following Specialist Completion - Within twenty-five (25) Working Days.*
Clause 20.12	Constructor valuation following Specialist Completion account - Within twenty-five (25) Working Days.
Clause 20.13	Constructor issue of Specialist Final Account following date/event stated in Specialist Agreement - Within twenty (20) Working Days.
Clause 20.14	Specialist dispute of Specialist Final Account, following issue - Within forty (40) Working Days.
Clause 20.15	Notice of proposed suspension of performance for non-payment - At least seven (7) days.
Clause 21.1	Notice of proposed Specialist Completion - At least seven (7) Working Days.*
Clause 21.2	Constructor confirmation as to whether Specialist Completion has been achieved following attendance/ inspection/testing - Within four (4) Working Days.
Clause 26.1	Notice of Specialist termination for non-achievement of pre-conditions - At least ten (10) Working Days.
Clause 26.1	Constructor notification of termination under clause 26.1 of Partnering Contract, following notice under that clause - Within five (5) Working Days.
Clause 26.3	Rectification of notified Specialist breach - Within ten (10) Working Days.
Clause 26.5	Rectification of notified Constructor breach - Within ten (10) Working Days.
Clause 26.7	Valuation following termination for Constructor bankruptcy/ insolvency/breach or following termination under Partnering Contract - Within fifteen (15) Working Days.
Clause 26.8	Constructor/Specialist agreement to avoid proposed suspension/ abandonment - Within twenty (20) Working Days.
Clause 26.10	Abandonment following suspension - Three (3) calendar months.

PPC2000 FLOWCHARTS

A.   Pre-Construction Phase Flowchart

B.   Construction Phase and Project Completion Flowchart

C.   Design and Process Development Flowchart (clause 8 of PPC2000 Partnering Terms)

D.   Supply Chain Development Flowchart (clause 10 of PPC2000 Partnering Terms)

E.   Price Development Flowchart (clause 12 of PPC2000 Partnering Terms)

F.   Change Flowchart (clause 17 of PPC2000 Partnering Terms)

G.   Risk Management Flowchart (clause 18 of PPC2000 Partnering Terms)

GUIDE to PPC2000 & SPC2000 © ACA and Trowers & Hamlins 2003

A. PRE-CONSTRUCTION PHASE FLOWCHART

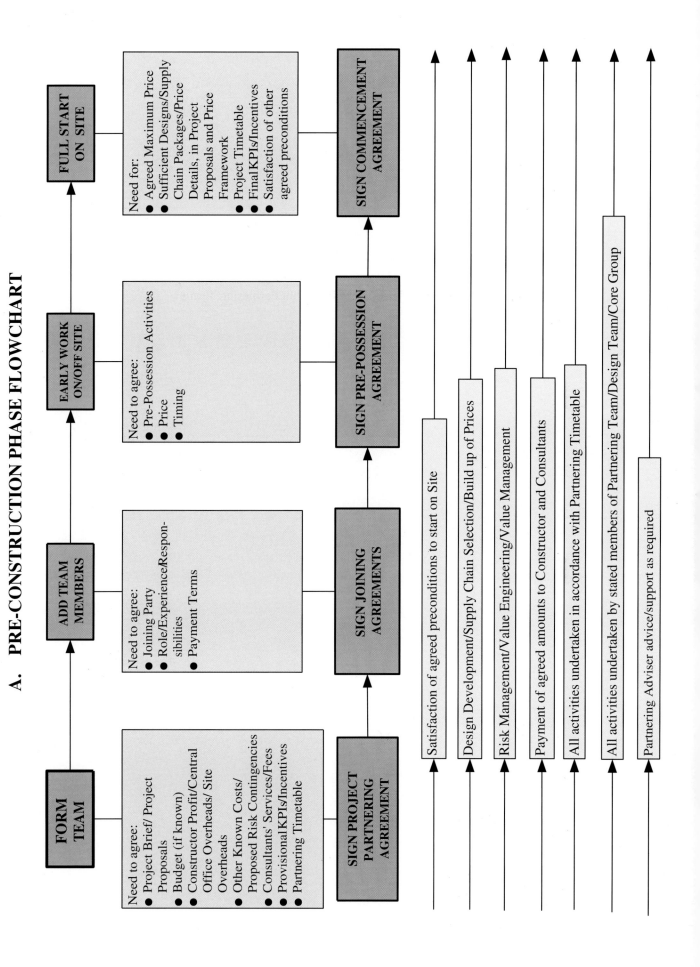

B. CONSTRUCTION PHASE AND PROJECT COMPLETION FLOWCHART

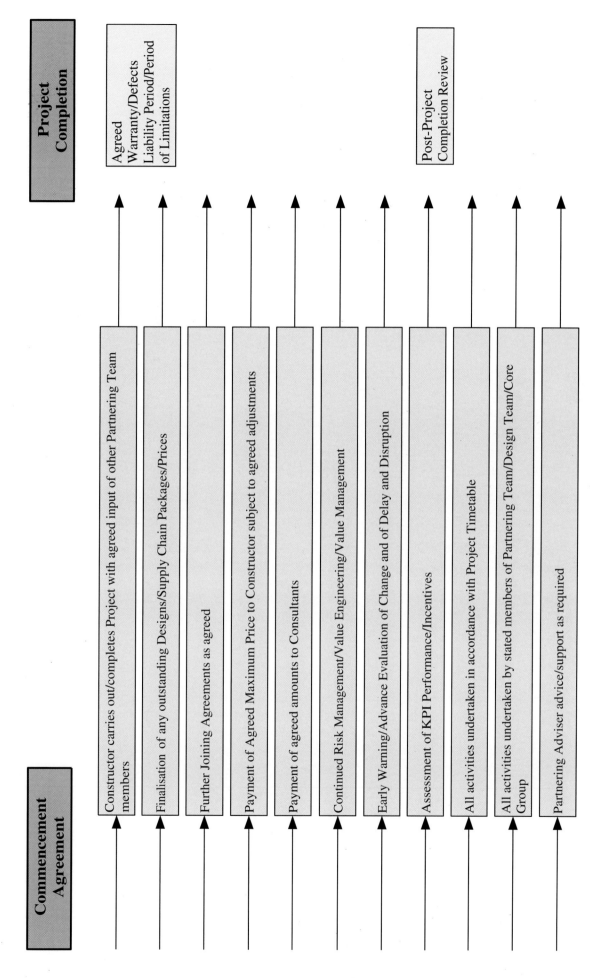

Commencement Agreement

Project Completion

Agreed Warranty/Defects Liability Period/Period of Limitations

Post-Project Completion Review

Constructor carries out/completes Project with agreed input of other Partnering Team members

Finalisation of any outstanding Designs/Supply Chain Packages/Prices

Further Joining Agreements as agreed

Payment of Agreed Maximum Price to Constructor subject to agreed adjustments

Payment of agreed amounts to Consultants

Continued Risk Management/Value Engineering/Value Management

Early Warning/Advance Evaluation of Change and of Delay and Disruption

Assessment of KPI Performance/Incentives

All activities undertaken in accordance with Project Timetable

All activities undertaken by stated members of Partnering Team/Design Team/Core Group

Partnering Adviser advice/support as required

C. DESIGN DEVELOPMENT FLOWCHART (Clause 8 of PPC2000 Partnering Terms)

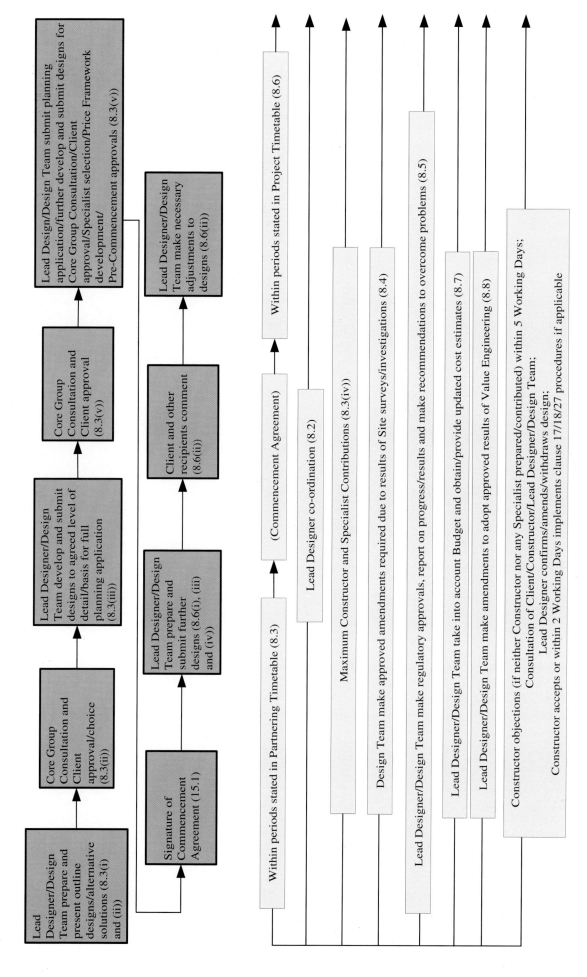

D. SUPPLY CHAIN DEVELOPMENT FLOWCHART
(Clause 10 of PPC2000 Partnering Terms)

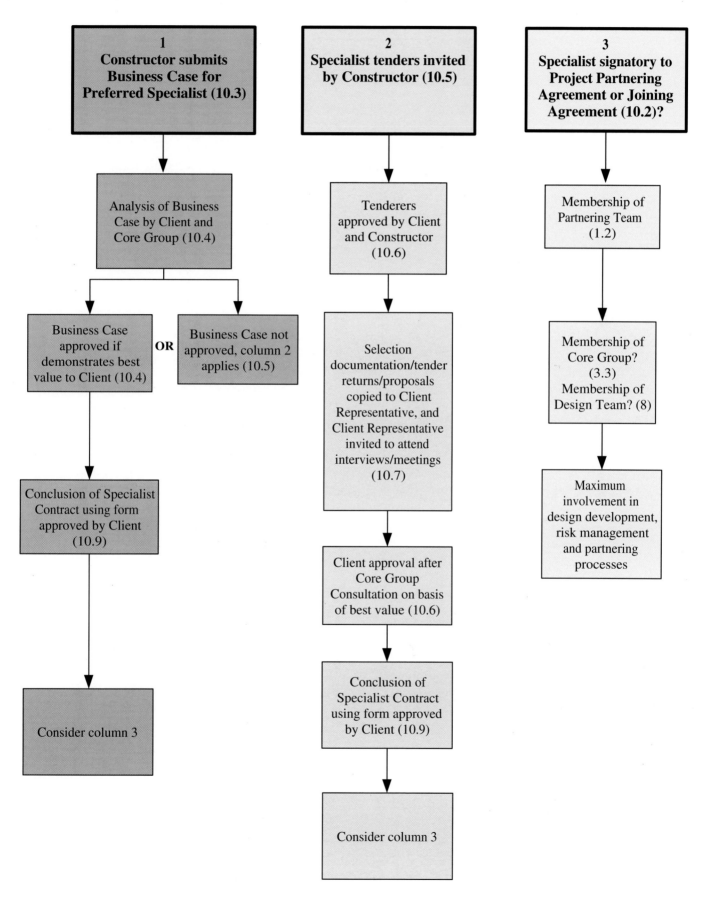

1
Constructor submits Business Case for Preferred Specialist (10.3)

Analysis of Business Case by Client and Core Group (10.4)

Business Case approved if demonstrates best value to Client (10.4)   **OR**   Business Case not approved, column 2 applies (10.5)

Conclusion of Specialist Contract using form approved by Client (10.9)

Consider column 3

2
Specialist tenders invited by Constructor (10.5)

Tenderers approved by Client and Constructor (10.6)

Selection documentation/tender returns/proposals copied to Client Representative, and Client Representative invited to attend interviews/meetings (10.7)

Client approval after Core Group Consultation on basis of best value (10.6)

Conclusion of Specialist Contract using form approved by Client (10.9)

Consider column 3

3
Specialist signatory to Project Partnering Agreement or Joining Agreement (10.2)?

Membership of Partnering Team (1.2)

Membership of Core Group? (3.3) Membership of Design Team? (8)

Maximum involvement in design development, risk management and partnering processes

E. PRICE DEVELOPMENT FLOWCHART (Clause 12 of PPC2000 Partnering Terms)

Project Partnering Agreement

Commencement Agreement

Price Framework comprising:

Agreed Constructor Profit, Central Office Overheads and Site Overheads (12.4)

Budget (12.3)

Any agreed amounts for fully designed and priced items/other known costs

Any agreed amounts for fully analysed/managed risks

Statement of proposed costing of risks including any prospective risk contingencies

Agreed payments to Constructor for Constructor Services and Pre-Possession Activities(12.1, 12.2)

Consultant Fees

Client approval of prices of Direct Labour Packages/Preferred Specialists/Specialist tenders (12.6 and 12.7)

Agreed adjustments pursuant to clause 13 (Incentives)

Risk Management to eliminate/reduce risk contingencies (12.9)

Agreed Maximum Price with detailed **Price Framework** (subject to any amounts agreed to be finalised during construction phase)

Agreed adjustments pursuant to Price Framework and clauses 13 (Incentives), 17 (Change), 18 (Risk Management)

Agreed adjustments pursuant to Consultant Payment Terms and clauses 13 (Incentives), 17 (Change), 18 (Risk Management)

F. CHANGE FLOWCHART
(Clause 17 of PPC2000 Partnering Terms)

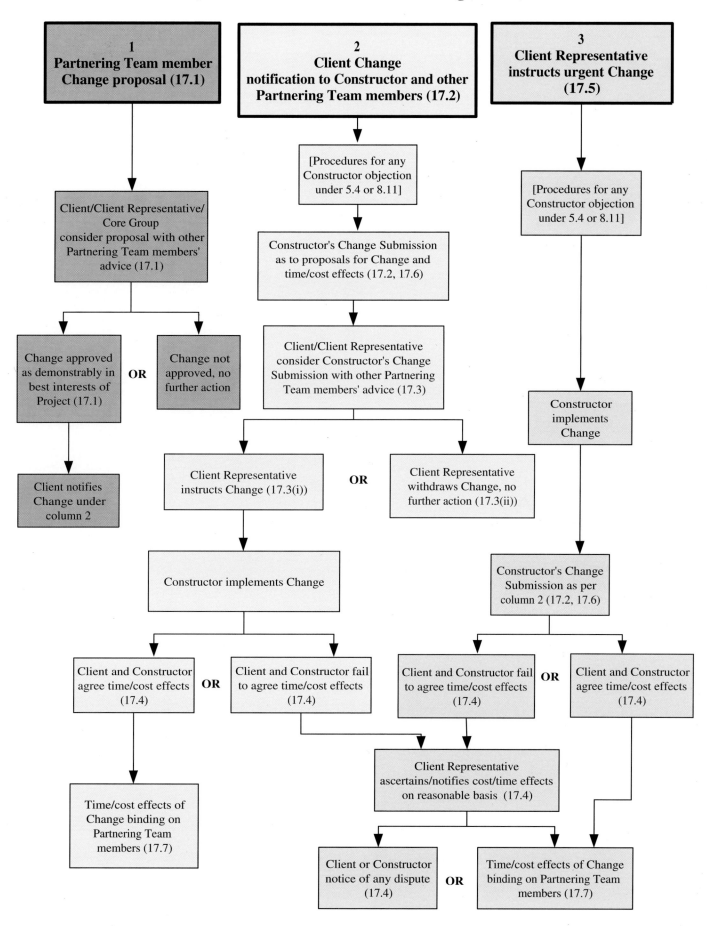

G. RISK MANAGEMENT FLOWCHART (Clause 18 of PPC2000 Partnering Terms)

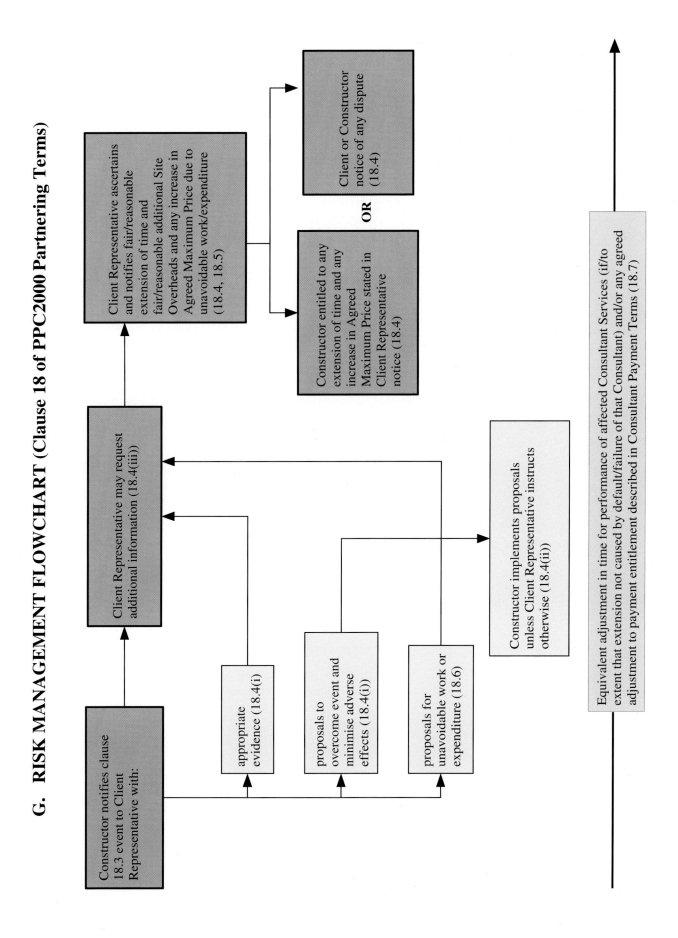